TRAUMA RESOLUTION

TRAINING IN TRAUMA COOPERATIVE YOGA® FOR SELF AND BEYOND

JOSEPHINE STANDING,
FOUNDER OF TCY®

Praise for Trauma Resolution: Training in TCY®

"As a Trauma and Wellness Specialist in private practice, I find this book serves as the first line of information that I share with both my colleagues and clients interested in body-felt trauma work. Her rare ability to blend academic neurobiological research with practitioner-based insights and personal reflection sets a standard in trauma scholarship." **Hank J. Brightman | Doctor of Education, Certified Clinical Trauma Professional**

"As a Cancer Survivor and Army Veteran, this book allowed me to go deep. I personally recommend this book to recover from past pain as well as for health professionals who want to rehab their clients back to optimal wellness. There are lessons for everyone on every learning curve in this great book!" **Brandi Benson | Author of 'Overcoming The Enemy Inside Me', United States Army Veteran, Speaker, and Sarcoma Survivor, Brandi Benson**

"As a therapist who has come to trust the body as a resource to process and resolve past pain, this book and its 200-hour Yoga Facilitation course are excellent tools. The teachings in body and mind fit seamlessly into my work. Even if one does not identify as having experienced trauma, the teachings include basic wellness truths. Ultimately, TCY® reinforces my relationship to myself, and for this I am grateful." **Jane Mizrahi | LICSW, RYT-200**

"A beautiful guide to the underutilized power of self-observation as a way to feel safe and allow the 'inner-standing' to shift from not knowing to healing." **Terry McBride | Co-Founder of YYoga Studios & Nettwerk Music**

“For many, both the trauma recovery process, and the moments leading up to active recovery, can feel somewhat like a war. This book makes the simple practice of TCY® accessible while it also awakens readers to the many levels of experience that occur throughout that process *no matter what kind of trauma one goes through.* Trauma is a part of all of our lives. and this book is therefore a ready gift for all.” **Kimie | Thought Leader and Founder of WorththeWar, Rethinking Love and Relationship www.WorthTheWar.com**

"This is **The Ultimate Guide** for any yoga practitioner who wants to better understand and lead survivors through a life changing experience of trauma recovery. From understanding the survivor's soul, experience, and how to move forward, you'll feel well prepared to support them as they navigate their personal journey on the yoga mat." **Kristie Overstreet | Ph.D., LPCC, LMHC, CST**

“Rome wasn’t built in a day, just as trauma doesn’t heal overnight. Within, you’ll find the groundwork for the practice of Trauma Cooperative Yoga®. This book by Jo equips both teachers, and survivors, with the methods necessary to shift through the collective trauma that can be so deeply embedded in our psyche. So, we may begin the practice of active recovery through TCY®. From the yoga mat and beyond, the ideas and concepts provided are an empowering reminder that healing, like Rome, is a result of laying one brick at a time.” **Joshua Ham | United States Army Paratrooper**

“Trauma Resolution: Training in Trauma Cooperative Yoga® For Self and Beyond is an important resource for any Yoga Teacher who desires to enhance their understanding of trauma and to feel more confident in their ability to facilitate Yoga classes with practitioners who may be experiencing the effects of trauma. Jo Standing presents TCY® as more than a system, but a mindset, an integrated approach of facilitating encouragement of safe-will movement and ‘innerstanding’ that soothes and empowers Yoga

practitioners. Grounded in research and experience, she provides a thorough explanation of the TCY® approach and concrete examples of how to apply its principles to your classes, all written in a way that is very approachable, digestible, and fun to read."
Jackie Jones | Owner of Flourish Momentum, Integrative Health and Wellness www.flourishmomentum.com

"The world is fortunate to be exposed to this masterpiece, 'Trauma Resolution'. It builds awareness of how you can prevent the possible re-causing of the 'inner simulation' of past episodic events. It is well-researched, and thoroughly-tested."
Alstria Compton | Chicago-born U.S. Army Chief Warrant Officer Veteran, Author of 'The Power of Persistence', and the Upcoming, 'Inside Threat'

"Jo Standing is courageously and profoundly dedicated to helping survivors safely reconnect to their body, heal their trauma, and engage more fully with their lives. This beautiful book is a testament to her life's work, and gently reminds us of the humbling reality of trauma. It offers a simple and holistic approach for professionals to expand the career of yoga sharing to work with individuals affected by psychological, and emotional, trauma. TCY offers a set of principles that support safety, dynamic support, and inclusivity; it is well-researched, evidence-based, and clinical-minded guidance to successfully facilitate helping move the unmetabolized trauma energy out of the nervous system for good."
Tracy-Michelle Kerouac | Reflexologist, Yogi, Supporter, Mother

"What I really appreciated about reading this book was the concept of a type of Yoga that meets you where you're at. Practical Yoga, I feel, is nearly non-existent in yoga teachings today. I've always been intimidated by Yoga. Yoga to me is primarily about that whole community thing, and being accepted into it. Also, it doesn't appear to be too welcoming to newcomers, and I felt judged if I couldn't perform the difficult Yoga postures being taught. In a word, Yoga to me was more or less a cult culture that you either fit into, or not. Although I know there are lots of benefits to it, I felt the access to those benefits had a price. A price *until now* that I was not willing to pay. This book not only restored my hope in the practice of Yoga, but it really simplified it, and expanded the practice into the amazing benefits to help those dealing with trauma. I couldn't be more thrilled to see the impact that this teaching will have on the Yoga community, especially those who can now benefit from its practice thanks to this work." **Raphael Verela | Founder of Circuit Works LA, United States Marine Corps Veteran**

"Jo continues to shine with her wealth of knowledge. She provides such practical guidance in an easy-to-implement blueprint with science backed breakthroughs. 'Trauma Resolution' highlights conscious ways to live with intention, and ceremony, and is sure to be a celebrated pathway toward grounded healing for many years to come." **Brandon Mills | Recon USMC Combat Veteran, Present Day Singer and Songwriter: Freedom Fighter for Liberty and Love**

"Through *Trauma Resolution*, Jo deftly breaks down the what, where, and why of our human experience with the skill of someone who has spent years perfecting their craft. The book reads exceptionally well for the veteran Yoga teacher, novice student, or practitioner who aims to better understand their own mind and the human environment inside and around themselves. Jo not only shares how trauma manifests within ourselves, but gives real-world examples of how we might address them in our own communities." **Phil Sussman | Co-Founder of American Yogi™, United States Army Veteran**

By the same author

Conquer Trauma Drama: Get Your Life Back
Conquer Trauma Drama: Breakthrough Curriculum

The author of this book does not dispense medical advice or prescribe the use of any technique as an absolute form of treatment for physical, mental, or emotional problems. The author, in alignment with governmental requirements, suggests you contact a doctor before implementing any of the advice, tips, or techniques in this book. The intent of the author is to offer information and entertainment to serve the reader on the quest for emotional, mental, physical, and spiritual well-being. In the event that you do use any or all of the information in this book for yourself or another, which is your constitutional right, the author, publisher, and all people mentioned herein on the pages of this book assume no responsibility for your actions. The author wishes you great fulfillment on the reading adventure forward.

For speaking opportunities, or TCY® training facilitation in a town near you, please contact the author with your proposal.
Book Cover: Carol Pearl
Print Edition: ISBN 978-0-578-97675-4
Kindle Edition: ISBN 978-0-578-97676-1

Acknowledgements

This book wouldn't be possible if it weren't for those who carved the way before my own journey into the endless field of learning about trauma resolution. However, I offer special thanks to those people who have striven to meet excellence where few have believed it possible, especially author **Judith Hermann.** In my life, through my own Post Traumatic Stress challenges, the wellness and academic advisors, psychic surgeons, and friends who are my family, this book is made visible. Thank you to my mother, **Penny,** who spent tireless hours focusing on my passion for writing during her weekends many years ago for the publication of my first fiction contribution to the world. Thank you to my husband, **Alex,** for caring enough to read much of my research leading up to this book. Thank you to my beta test group for dedicating 12 weekends, beginning each day at or before sunrise, in order to become the world's first **TCY® facilitators.** Thank you to social worker and therapist, **Jane Mizrahi,** for using your professionality to buoy the life of this work in your fearless dive *heart first* into its depths... **A deep Namaste bow to the American warriors-in-uniform**: I consider myself lucky to bear witness to both the hardships *and* glories ignited by trauma itself.

Thank you to **Karen Stupski at Goddard College** for seeing all angles, to **Terry McBride** for artfully living his bliss, to **Pat Black** for sharing her Northern California land, to **Ren Jones** for pointing toward the horizon, to **Dr. Kristie Overstreet** for sharing her valuable inward connection, to **Brandi Benson** for stepping up, **United States Military Service Members: Raphael Verela, Alstria Compton, Joshua Ham, Brandon Mills, Phil Sussman for believing,** to **Jackie Jones** for caring so deeply, **Dr. Hank Brightman** for keeping up with the good fight, **United States Military**

Veterans, Isaiah Perez, Daniel Chism, Enrique Irby, and Donald Mcalister for helping to lead the way, and for the endless road trips and global trots that brought me closer to the pulse and shine of humanity. To all of those who believe Yoga has a place both in Herstory, and History, thank you for supporting this work. Special thanks to **Angel Melendez of Chicago** for his cinematic work, and therefore further bringing this work alive on YouTube, and our online Training platform InnerBeatYoga.com.

Table of Contents

Foreword 1

Part One | Working with the Soul of the Survivor 2

Chapter 1 - What You Need to Know 3

Chapter 2: Voicing Emotions with Empathy 11

Chapter 3: The Cornerstones of Teaching TCY® 13

Chapter 4: A Glimpse into The Trauma Survivor's Nervous System 26

Chapter 5: Cultivating Healthy Power Dynamics in the Classroom 35

Chapter 6: The Pillars of Language-Building 61

Chapter 7: Constructing Language: A Tool for Creating Healthy Sense of Self in Trauma Cooperative Yoga® 72

Part Two | Becoming the Soul of the Survivor 88

Chapter 8: Learning the Survivor's Experience 89

Chapter 9: Successfully Building a Sense of Containment: Security and Safety on The Trauma Cooperative Yoga® mat 115

Chapter 10: Breath Mastery as an Integral Part of Self-Healing 129

Chapter 11: Transparency of Experience 140

Part Three | Navigating Forward Motion 146

Chapter 12: Holding "Valid" Space as Teachers and Facilitators 147

Chapter 13: How to Work Within Scope of Practice 152

Chapter 14: How to Work with the Autonomic Nervous System States 155

Chapter 15: The Specifics of Trauma Cooperative Yoga® 166

Chapter 16: Meditation as a Daily Practice 187

Chapter 17: Managing the Psyche Soma Pain Threshold in Trauma Cooperative Yoga® 195

Chapter 18: Social and Ecological Justice as Applied to Trauma Cooperative Yoga® 211

Bibliography 233

About The Author 243

Foreword

This book is intended for educational purposes with the "innerstanding" that what you know within you amplifies what you might come to understand through the reading of this book. Everything written in here is an invitation to pursue the knowledge and wisdom within you. Yoga teachers and yoga facilitators need to know more about the human condition post-trauma, and this work is an invitation to you to keep seeking within yourself to discover and resolve the impact of traumatic life experiences in your own life and in the lives of those in your community. It is a call to you to awaken your imaginative, researched, and willful self-examinations. Through continuing to put one foot in front of the other we learn what is possible when we remove the chains of the past's influence in our lives. Let us live for today, and its discoveries. Now.

Part One |

Working with the Soul of the Survivor

Chapter 1 - What You Need to Know

Laying the Groundwork

Welcome to the ultimate guide to becoming a Trauma Cooperative Yoga® practitioner for the personal and collective gain of long lasting health. It has been said by some researchers that the human brain can only absorb 45 minutes straight of information. Then, it tends to shut down. So, it might be best to read this book in increments where you perhaps dedicate a half or whole day every weekend to set aside, create sacred space with your favorite pillows, scents, coffee or teas, and juices and snacks readily available nearby, in order to feed the best possible experience. Then, you might take fifteen minutes every now and then as breaks. Perhaps, planning one every forty-five minutes in order to iron out any tensions in the body or mind, take a stroll, play with your pets, or practice some postures/breathing/meditation. When appropriate, you might want to try and make this FUN! You'll go a lot further with the information if you do so.

Intro to the Core of Trauma Cooperative Yoga®

Trauma Cooperative Yoga® facilitation allows practitioners and facilitators to move outside of the regular norms such as the notion that we always practice "om" from seated, or the occasional "om" from standing. TCY® might also challenge that the best posture to collect yourself in or press pause in is undoubtedly downward facing dog, or child's posture, as they are traditionally called. In Trauma Cooperative Yoga® self-determination replaces the heavy amount of self-discipline that is often called upon in traditional yoga classes. Instead the teacher, or facilitator, led encouragement for the practitioner to learn to listen to their inner-callings is strongly present. This philosophical shift from heavy emphasis on self-discipline, to self-determination, is made possible by the giving of safe practicing constructs and are made known at the beginning of each class, as well as offered throughout. This is so that the practitioner is operating from a place of growing self-awareness that includes the basic safety knowledge for injury prevention. Class participation centers around tuning into self-care principles instead of following every yoga posture that the facilitator is guiding at any given moment. Trauma Cooperative Yoga® can include self-adjustments, as detailed by the facilitator, for optimal personal support in each posture, and the intrinsic growth point of self-initiation. Variables of self-care, or self-soothing, are also offered up by the facilitator in the postures. All postures are optional at all times.

TCY® is about meeting the practice of yoga on your own terms so that you as a practitioner may also learn to live life off the mat in a way that encourages you as a trauma survivor to manage the present symptoms of post traumatic stress, however latent they may be. Whether the trauma(s) was recent, or if one is experiencing a relapse into post traumatic stress, the practice helps to prevent too intense of a symptom relapse. Although we cannot always feel control over when we feel anxiety, stress, or depression, or any other cornerstone of post traumatic stress, with enough self-knowledge, and environments that encourage such self-connection, we can rise from potential relapse with more grit, and personal wherewithal, without losing too many of our days, weeks, months, and/or years.

Why the Trauma Cooperative Yoga® Approach is Essential

For many years myself and teachers around the world have been told that we must be some shade or variation of perfection in our teaching. It has made our time with our practitioners next to contrived if nothing else than insensitive to what we as people, *and yes as teachers,* are experiencing in each moment. This intensity of anatomical exactness as a teacher has created an equally as negatively impactful void in understanding ourselves and our practitioners in deeper ways, as well as our relationships with our practitioners. In so many words, we as universal yoga practitioners are told to acknowledge our feelings from an awareness place rather than from an embodied and expressed place. Whereas feelings are like clouds that come and go, and we observe them, we have yet to be educated on the mat on how we respond proactively to the emotional and mental dispositions of ourselves in order to then align with the best and most integrated versions of ourselves.

Whether we identify ourselves as an instructor, teacher, and/or facilitator of yoga we must realize that as we navigate the Trauma Cooperative Yoga® world in the yoga classroom we are most benefited from being geared toward "not knowing" in regards to the personal nuances of the survivor's experience while also possessing an educational background of the trauma survivor's experience, such as this book provides. We are most well served by allowing our courage to embrace the unknown to flourish mostly because it opens new gateways to more accurately innerstanding how to show up for the survivors in our classes. When we attend yoga classes as a trauma survivor of any kind we are often faced with the false need to appear perfect in an anatomical fashion, all the while with this mindset we distance both the practitioners from greater knowing of themselves, on all levels, as well as ourselves as facilitators from the value of unity, or "yoking" that yoga is built upon.

Practitioners of yoga often seek to put the best impression of themselves forward while following the teacher. It is to the detriment of any trauma survivor to try and conform to what another person expects of one's bodily experience. There is no exception to this. The moment that a survivor cuts off from their own felt body experience in order to please the teacher's cueing is the instance that the practitioner now unplugs from their inner guidance system. As Trauma Cooperative Yoga® facilitators it is our duty to be transparent enough to show what it is we are going through in the moment in order to best teach and relay the teachings of yoga. It takes a certain kind of brave individual to arrange a setting where they are being proactive to share their inner experience so that others might *just maybe* benefit from it.

Yet, this is exactly what is needed in order to support the internal wholing and self-healing of trauma survivors. The decision to listen inwardly sits on a new horizon that is within reach. We have names for people who listen *to themselves* versus the odds as quoted by others as a pre-step to taking any kind of action in their life. We call them brave, courageous, amazing, stupendous, unlike-any-other, etc. The truth is we all have that capability and it is up to us to nurture that initiative of deep inner listening within our practitioners so that they may then find their way in an increasingly loud and bustling world.

The Yogi's Ultimate Alignment

In yoga class we as facilitators have the ultimate challenge to decide why we are there to share the art of yoga as it has evolved from the lineages. Are we there to instruct people, teach people, or to facilitate the experience of yoga? Or, is it a combination of all of the above depending on the circumstances, nature of the attendees, and the class description? **To instruct someone** means that we are guiding them primarily more times than not on the movement of their limbs alone, and we're passing down the same instructions that were given to us, without too much additional thought. **As teachers,** we are educating on why such movements are suggested with the perk of mentioning the benefits of the practitioners doing so. **As a facilitator,** we furthermore work to create circumstances that empower the practitioner to choose the direction of their own knowing *while* maintaining the core of the spiritual practice of self-realization and supporting a safe practice experience.

Of course, as teachers it is incredibly normal and acceptable to be concerned about taking new approaches. It is okay to be concerned that by approaching the class with a zeal for promoting newfound freedom on the mat for what the practitioner chooses to partake in, and not partake in, is new and therefore also might feel radical. Yet, perhaps with these simple changes in the approach to facilitating yoga classes we are being the anchor that encourages the key distinction between align, or define. When we align with our power as teachers instead of allowing that power to define us we open the gateway for our practitioners to have the chance to know their own positive personal power.

In a world focused on outward realities, life can be extremely limited on the chances to recenter oneself to become fully acquainted with one's own inner power as defined by oneself. With this lack of self-knowledge, power itself can take on a jaded or skeptical appearance in one's mind. In today's time, we have become growingly weary of discussions around power itself as an explorative construct because of toxic power, and the negative use of power, in the world, adversely impacting people. As people, in and out of the classroom, we can mistake the pursuit of power as being selfish or egotistical and this is often because so few people sit to contemplate how they may develop and exercise their inner sense of power as it relates to itself, and to one's personal development, rather than in the influencing of others.

In the Trauma Cooperative Yoga® classroom we are asking people to become alliances with their inner sense of power. We are asking people to become growingly aware of their thoughts instead of washing them away with the sound of their breath, or asking them to observe their thoughts as if they are clouds passing by, as we so often have heard in the yoga classroom. With the use of open-ended questions in the holding of postures, and the request to hold positive self-affirmations in the body movement itself, the power of the mind is befriended, instead of seen as a non-integral piece of the yogic pie. No matter what we choose to say and do in the anticipated safe space of the yoga classroom, let us best serve the people in our classroom as an encourager, and guide, to greater inner space and knowing.

Acknowledge and Announce

In an intimate conversation with *Sounds True Publishing & Podcasts* founder, Tami Simon, author and scientist, Jill Bolte Taylor, does a great job at normalizing the occurrence of any and all kinds of feelings that arise in our practice of yoga both on and off of the mat. Dr. Jill Bolte Taylor describes this process as, "Nurture that circuitry." She talks about allowing herself to feel and that *each emotion* she has is merely a circuit. "I see it as a circuit that needs to run." she shares. However, "I need to have the clarity of mind *to decide* what I am going to do with it." In essence, "We are emotional beings having a cognitive experience." If you ever get the chance to hear her speak or read any of her books, she informatively describes how the limbic brain experiences things first *then* comes the logistical process. Furthermore, "If we don't feel safe then our hippocampus shuts off, and we consequently can not learn."

Therefore we need to *feel safe* in order to learn and grow, no matter who we are, where our beginnings originated, or how lofty our paths have become at present.

As we take these thoughts by Dr. Bolte Taylor into consideration and then move forward with clarity of mind, and mental presence, we become aware that if we're triggered at any point during the regular day, in an unfamiliar setting, or in our yoga class, we may then *acknowledge and announce.* First we acknowledge what is wrong on a feeling level since as Dr. Bolte says feelings are how we firstly process the world. Then, upon noticing we use our concerted mental strength to notate the internal *bodily* feeling that we are having in that moment. This is the acknowledgement phase. Then, a silent speaking to the self through any one or a mixture of the following: quiet internal dialogue, making physical contact with the self in that moment to reinforce self-care, a soft om, or if pen and paper are present beside the mat then taking time to write down a life-giving affirmation. The affirmation is to serve the function to acknowledge the challenge, announce the desired new direction, and atone for the difference between the two with a final acceptance statement. A life-giving affirmation is one that enlightens you and guides you to continue to move in the emotional, mental, physical and/or spiritual direction of your highest intent and order.

So, What is Meant by Sensitive, Anyway?

What does it mean to be sensitive? Since it is often used as a term in yoga teaching it is crucial that we do an exploration behind what it means before we begin covering any of the yoga philosophy or the history of trauma, or of yoga itself, for that matter. Oftentimes people see being sensitive as a weakness. Or, it is perceived as a fearful component of one's self because of what it often translates to if someone doesn't yet know how to deal with the experience of sensitivity in an astute and productive manner. As people we've likely either been called "too sensitive" or "not sensitive enough" aka not having any Emotional Intelligence as coined by researchers, Peter Salavoy and John Mayer, in 1990.

Speaking of EQ, even corporations are now considering what the human factor of emotion is in the room when deciding how they will deliver certain power points or company briefings. Now, of course, we can use feeling and the awareness of feeling for the benefit of people OR we can use it for the demise of people. Therefore, which person or facilitator would you rather be? Human emotion is oftentimes perceived as being very delicate. The reality is that people, when educated on the function of feeling, can take their lives in awesome directions and support others in making the best choices for their lives, and all based on positive feeling.

There have been studies done that show that whether people are under the tutelage of someone who is supportive and space giving, or on the contrary under the tutelage of someone who is constantly questioning your actions and saying, "you can do it better" determines if the practitioner will succeed, or not. Of course, we all need a positive push in the right direction with constructive and encouraging words. However, if the practitioner is being drawn away from their own decision-making compass, time and time again, then they will begin to doubt themselves and consequently the relationship between themselves and the teacher. That study is in the book *"Originals"* by Adam Grant. It's a definite read, by the way! Anyway, moving forward it is key to understand firstly that your job as a TCY® facilitator is to become sensitive to the people in front of you according to the knowledge their actions, and inactions, are telling you. The practitioners in your care are there to become greatly connected to their own presence. They might not say that. In fact, they most likely will not. However, everyone dreams of being the most enlightened version of themselves and that doesn't always mean, or even *ever* mean, doing the most advanced version of a posture. It is vital that we treat practitioners with that respect especially if you get the sense that no one else might've done so before you. People *will* wake up to themselves if you give them the chance.

As a facilitator, watch your inner workings and notice and hold yourself accountable for becoming sensitive to the fact that you're a leader in the classroom. Everything you do and say matters. There's no caveat to that. It's the great role of a teacher that requires total presence and connection to your intention to lead a Trauma Cooperative Yoga® class that allows you to connect deeply with your practitioners and create an experience that they will never forget. Now, is there room for humor, laughter, and joy in the classroom? Definitely, I think so! However, if there's humor you best make sure it is a result of reflecting on yourself, and your own life and ways of being, versus pointed toward any of your unexpecting practitioners. This concludes your brief introduction to sensitivity. Let's keep moving forward to the next lesson in place.

Chapter 2: Voicing Emotions with Empathy

Teaching from Empathy versus Sympathy

OK, you're on a roll...let's jump right in! For starters, it is key to mention that having empathy does not mean that you are saying you know what someone else is going through. In fact, having empathy and showing empathy are two very different things. Just as what we say and how we say it are two different key components to human interaction, we might already be quite proficient at feeling empathy but being empathetic might very likely be a skill we are still working on. Another key misunderstanding in the expression of empathy: showing empathy does not mean finishing another's thoughts. This sometimes might look like, "...Yes, I know exactly how you feel. It's like ____." The ____ usually entails the telling of when you had an experience like that person. It's not that these are inherently bad approaches to empathy, it's just that they are not the actual definition of being empathetic, and knowing the difference is key for a "space holder" aka facilitator of TCY®.

If you're with friends and family the example given might very likely work. But, in the case of your practitioners and clients a new level of understanding of what it means to be empathetic is required for successful Trauma Cooperative Yoga® facilitation. So, what is the dictionary-based definition of being empathetic, anyway? Merriam Webster says... "the action of understanding, being aware of, being sensitive to, and vicariously experiencing the feelings, thoughts, and experience of another of either the past or present without having the feelings, thoughts, and experience fully communicated in an objectively explicit manner." By 'explicit' it means that we are not doing any of the above that I mentioned, whether it's saying we know or filling in their blanks. So, now, let's look at what it means to be empathetic in this study of self and TCY®.

In the classroom, if someone looks like they're too depressed or anxious to practice a suggested posture then we must go within ourselves as leaders, and within our own accumulated knowledge base, to consider mentioning to the class that if anyone is feeling too tired ('too tired' is a neutral, non-clinical/non-diagnosing, non-triggering alternative to the word 'depressed') or restless ('restless' is a neutral, non-clinical, non-triggering alternative to the word 'anxious' or "anxiety-ridden") that they may or may not want to experiment with practicing _______. This is where you give the practitioner(s) an alternative to the current posture you've invited them to practice *without* calling them out.

An Exercise of Showing Empathy

You see, seeking to understand what the practitioner might be feeling based on their body language and/or lack thereof throughout the class will give you a strength otherwise known as actualized, or activated, empathy. It's not just a mirroring of feelings now, it's an action. The word sympathy existed in our culture for several hundred years before empathy for a reason. The practice of being empathetic is just that, a newer practice, and a developmental tool to building trust and confidence in you as a facilitator.

Chapter 3: The Cornerstones of Teaching TCY®

In a pinch, if you're ever feeling stressed or worried about delivering a solid Trauma Cooperative Yoga® class to your class attendees, put the simple acronym, M.A.T. in the back of your mind to draw upon. Scientifically speaking, it is of course the conscious front of your mind otherwise known as the frontal lobe. This evolution of how to best honor people most affected by trauma is exactly just that. It takes time, and as your brain continues to sense the impact of your words and actions on your class' attending practitioners then you will widen your toolbelt with your newest observations. If, or when, we work "in the light" with the best intentions to bring people closer to the center point of inner power then our collective practice as facilitators continues to grow and shift.

Just as everything in this world is meant to evolve, and will do so whether we like our old ways, or not, yoga also requires extra considerations as a reflection to the changing times. This willingness to try something new is the basis for your continual greatness as a facilitator. People in your class will be thankful to you no matter if it's teaching to the local women's and children's shelter, men's transition house, a gymnasium of police recruits, firefighters, at a local Veteran's Affairs office, or from your own studio, where you highlight a day a week for Trauma Cooperative Yoga® classes.

Now, here is the acronym to keep in mind for starters for now:

M.A.T.

M = Meet Inner Needs

A = Actively Self-Soothe

T = Take Initiative

Here's why each of these are vital to the wellbeing of the trauma survivors in your classroom and each will be explored at greater length throughout this book.

M = Meet Inner Needs

Trauma survivors are often existing in the freeze state of the fight, flight, freeze phenomenon. In fact, studies have shown that people who have frozen during the time of their trauma are more likely to become adversely affected by Post Traumatic Stress. In addition, that state of freezing comes and goes throughout random times of the day. Therefore, although it is extremely challenging to assess what one's needs even are in the present moment, due to the complexity of the disposition of freezing itself, and the lack of connection that comes about as a result, *it is exactly what a survivor must figure* out in order to gain both temporary and long term freedom within their lives. This reacquainting with the self rightfully takes time. In addition, it takes a gently persistent teacher to remind the practitioner to continue to tune-in, instead of tuning out as the survivor is so often inclined. In this book, you will find ways to do that for each of your class attendees.

A = Actively Self-Soothe

Self-care is oftentimes at the bottom of the list for trauma survivors as an actual action that is successfully lived out. This is not intentional, in fact most people, whether they've gone through extreme hell or not, tend to speak of physical care goals, whether it's physical fitness, or diet. However, when it boils down to actually embodying those goals the mental stamina or mental presence, simply has yet to be enforced in order to create long lasting change. However capable people are of enacting those changes as they are often simple in theory such as getting to the physical fitness class, or the social event, or making fresh juice a part of every morning, the *doing* of them isn't always a reality. This is due to a lack of mind presencing exercises in one's life.

This is where Trauma Cooperative Yoga® holds yet another strength. Through encouraging and educating *how* the practitioner may self-soothe in each practiced posture, or meditation, we are further instilling the possibility that the presence of mind just might become a regular occurrence in the practitioner's life off of the mat. Presence of mind, or mind presencing, positively enables a person to go 180 degrees in the opposite direction from where they currently stand without the struggle, nor personal suffering, that accompanies focusing on a problem. A present mind that is conditioned to be both present *and ready* to alter the current state of experience doesn't get stuck in self-blame, self-judgment, or self-ridicule.

A mind trained in mind presencing simply observes what-is, and from there re-orders the focus of the presence moment to one that is life-giving by being in alignment with one's needs. Now, it is hopefully easier to feel your way as a teacher, guide, and facilitator, why the offering of self-soothing techniques is of the essence in a Trauma Cooperative Yoga® setting. As you read this book, keep in mind that you are educating people through a friendly and ready mind to become cooperative with their own trauma. That can look a million different ways depending on the practitioner's life experiences.

T = Take Initiative

When change or experience is forced upon us, versus us having free will where we can otherwise choose a path of action that is non-forceful, we lose our sense of our positive inner power. The idea of power in an archaic sense is the ability to influence the world around you. However, as we evolve as humans the idea of power shifts and becomes an aspect of self that exists whether or not we are able to change our environment in an instant, or ever. As we know, local and nationwide laws can impede our ability to perhaps see the world as we might like it to be--whatever that means to you, whether it's your opinion on gun control, or the right to smoke marijuana. However, when we are passionate about something, even as it relates to the physical world beyond our own inner power, every effort towards remedying the perceived problem builds our ability to believe in ourselves, and take personal just action in our own lives, no matter who is on our side of the fence, in the ring with you, or not. This is the beauty of the inner power that allows us to take initiative in our lives.

When we are without knowledge of this inner self, or of this inner power, we lack the ability to take steadfast action in our lives, and this disposition often shows on the yoga mat, just as all the other parts of self often do. Understanding our needs, and soothing ourselves in a moment of feeling overwhelmed, anxious, or powerless are indeed the foundations for then finding a way to take initiative to make any given situation one that favors and builds into you. There is no reason for a trauma survivor to reinforce helplessness as again is often the case with trauma survivors in a traditional yoga class format. Therefore, as teachers, guides, and facilitators, as we show up on the mat our best thought investment in order to do everything in our divine power to ensure against this form of inner enslavement that occurs within trauma survivors is to authentically share our next steps with the classroom with an open mind that the practitioner is likely, *if not encouraged,* to find the best version of the practice of yoga in that moment for themself.

So, how do we do this for our class practitioners? The ins and outs of that are included herein.

Invitation versus Cue

The first thing that people need to know about trauma survivors is that more often than not they want nothing more than to feel normal like everyone else. This means you say *"Jump"* and they say, *"How high?"* This is incredibly dangerous in a Yoga classroom. As trauma resilience leader Judith Hermann stands behind wholeheartedly, and as all trauma survivors know too well, "Choice is the one missing component of any traumatic event." Choice usually was or is taken away at the time of a trauma. That said, with children since choice usually isn't understood as an option since children are raised to do as they are told, or in earlier decades, "Children are not to be heard", if or when a traumatic event occurred as a child the clarity around whether or not they actively chose -- or just surrendered to the traumatic reality -- is often confusing.

All this considered, for the sake of clear learning, let's focus on traumatic events being an experience where the overall function of choice, to take action or protect oneself in a way that might change the outcome of the immediate situation, is oftentimes a non-factor for the survivor. In reality choice simply doesn't exist in some life scenarios when someone else is inflicting their will against another. In the event where, for whatever reason, the individual often referred to in the English language as 'the victim' does not have a choice, then choice itself becomes all one has to recover oneself from the original trauma.

It is therefore our job as yoga classroom leaders to invite choice *in all things.* If someone doesn't want a choice and all they do is follow along with all your suggestions, without first checking in with their own bodies, then that is also in its own way their definite choice to be without one. In other words, you might exhibit your own choice in a transparent way where you might vocalize a change in choice as you demonstrate a posture with some words effective to, "Oh, wait - I feel a little tightness in here (pointing to the place) I am going to practice this variation of the posture, or self-soothe from here, instead." The best way we can lead is to bring people ***into our experiences*** in a professional way that firsthand shows people they have choices, you have choices, and you're unafraid to make those choices. Yes, even if and especially if it means coming up against an uncomfortable truth in the body.

In general, do everything you can in your presence to encourage choice while also remaining healthily detached that people have their own process and a lot of the issue of exercising choice might be in the fact that the practitioner simply needs to have A) more experience practicing on the mat. B) more experience inhabiting their body. C) has never been sensitive to their body in the first place because it's been known or is known as a dangerous place. Breaking these habits of disconnection or dissociation, freezing, or numbing is a process that needs to be honored. As David Emerson with the Justice Resource Institute in the United States points out it is key to honor even the seemingly negative coping mechanisms because they are there for a reason. All walls erode over time, but they need to crumble in their own time in order to keep a healthy mind-body balance of homeostasis as much as possible.

Encourage, and Honor, Natural Breath

In countless traditional yoga classes around the world people are often asked to follow a specific breath pattern. However, in a Trauma Cooperative Yoga® class we instead honor the personal embodiment and expression of breath. Our concern is not if they're inhaling and exhaling when you tell them to do so. Instead, it is whether or not the practitioner is connected to their own breath. This means they're not connected to how you think they 'should' breathe for maximum effectiveness of the posture nor for the perceived energetic or calming gains of the breath. It instead means that they are guided in simple ways to maintain an honest connection with what is natural for them in the moment. 'The body knows all,' we are told by our holistic practitioners of all modalities. 'The answers are inside of the body' we have heard over and over. 'Trust your body', we encourage as teachers, guides, and facilitators.

The cues for breathing in a Trauma Cooperative Yoga® class are boiled down to the cue to listen to one's own breath, pay attention to it, notice it, and allow it to move as it already is. The lengthening of one's breath or shortening of one's breath is best to be referred to as the facilitator sharing what they're practicing within their own breath, and why, for practitioners to then experiment and try on their own accord. Now, if you notice someone doing fire breathing breath at great length then you will of course, in a general information fashion, tell the class that by practicing fire breath too long it might awaken one's energy to such an extent that it might lead to feeling out of sorts from oneself, or overwhelmed. Notice, both are not clinical references. Both are human experiences that are relatable, and easy to connect with.

In the same fashion, as a facilitator, you might then follow those words with a reminder of a key breath that calms. You might also go to the length of demonstrating this calming breath. When it comes to whether or not we want people to breathe for a certain amount of counts on the inhale or exhale that is intended for a traditional class. It has no place in a room of Trauma Cooperative Yoga® practitioners. The number one modus operandi is to return people to the fact that there is a life force of breath that is beneath everything that we do. This life force of breath is intended to support all people to carry themselves throughout the day with more ease both on and off the mat.

It serves to tell people from the start of class that they are an instrument of their breath; they will have as much energy and support in their practice as they need or seek so long as they are tuned into their own breath. On the flipside, the reason why we are refraining from instructing people to breathe a certain way is because of the inherent disconnect, and the residual shame that is a byproduct of that disconnect. The nature of distrusting one's own body is the foundation for the disconnect that happens for trauma survivors in the day to day, and also is the purpose of this request of you as a Trauma Cooperative Yoga® facilitator-in-training. The body is already sending so many mixed signals that can *and often are* quite frightening for the trauma survivor. When you add-in cues to breathe a different way than one already is, it can be emotionally unsettling, and unintentionally cause panic, confusion, and fear not only in a felt sense but in the mind. The question that unwillfully arises in the practitioners' minds is, "Am I doing something wrong?"

In these limited scenarios, the resulting distrust of the body only deepens for the trauma survivor. Worse yet, there becomes a split between allowing oneself to feel and respond to what they genuinely and authentically are already *feeling* on the yoga mat, and what they are physically *doing.* This only adds to the internal division of the self. At the time of a trauma the experiencer of trauma often leaves all awareness of the body, or 'is beside themself', and instead focuses on the world and circumstances outside of them. This is a time when separation from self is most felt in the experience of the survivor.

How then as yoga facilitators may we continuously offer up the chance of self-connection? We need to look at all angles, including breath.

As teachers we need to make sure that we are enormously aware of our desire to control the experience of those on the mat. This is not said in a dark way. But, with the mind that "teacher knows best". However, this mentality is a dis-service to the Trauma

Cooperative Yoga® approach. Since breath is at the forefront of all yoga experiences, it is within the breath that we might most encourage people to claim the natural flow of their own life force aka breathing patterns. In other words, honor the rate at which they take in the world, and expel the world from their bodies, using their inhale and exhale as a primary tool.

With awareness, and a ton of practice, we know as yoga practitioners, whether we teach or facilitate, or not, that the accumulated life experiences, the amassing of feelings and sensations that we pick up on, in our day-to-day lives, and even in our personally-crafted worlds, fit to our liking, that so much is gained, as well as freed through our choiceful breathing. How we breathe is life-altering. We know this.

The rate of change and adaptation to the now safe world around you, as a trauma survivor, needs to be *the survivor's* choice. As facilitators it is our responsibility to do everything in our power to support the survivor to feel connected to, and in control of, their own bodies. People are known to do more than what their body or mind is able to do on the yoga mat simply because of a disoriented perspective of what matters most in the moment. However, in the larger picture, this far from makes them less than, or incapable of personally-oriented intelligence. As Dr. Daniel J. Libby says, "What we really want to do is live in alignment with our values and goals." And, Dr. Timothy Avery follows with, "Anxiety can get in the way of living those values and goals." Therefore, if practitioners are anxious to please the teacher it can wreak all kinds of havoc on them.

It is key to remember the caveat of TCY® facilitation that whereas we are not telling anyone how to breathe *we are sharing how it best serves us*, as leading practitioners alongside them, to breathe in each moment. We may therefore tell our practitioners what it is that we are doing with our breath with the intent to best serve their own growing awareness. For example, "I am feeling low energy right now so I am choosing to change up my breath by taking a series of ten short exhales following a long inhale. This is serving to quicken my blood flow, and provide more oxygen faster to my brain, muscles, and the rest of my organs." Or, "I am feeling anxious suddenly, so as I practice this posture I am extending my exhale longer than my inhale." And then say, "Keep in mind if you're ever feeling anxious in class you may practice this way, too. Once you feel what you are seeking to feel then I encourage you to return to your natural, uncontrolled, yet intentional, breath." In so many words. Then, you might add a refresher of intent, "Remember, so long as we are aware of our breath landing in our bodies we are maintaining the much needed connection to our bodies."

A final word on this: remember the last thing we want to do is shock anyone in the re-acclimatization to their body. A quick, seemingly-harmless, cue to tell them to breathe in a certain cadence or for any length of time can create confusion, panic, and only reinforce that frozen state of fear that they likely might have known during their trauma(s).

The Difference Between the Brain and Mind

To be human means many things and includes having the luxury, or hindrance, depending on how one looks at it, of having both a brain *and* a mind. The mind is often called "The Monkey Mind" in Yoga including in some of the *Bhagavad Gita* translations. The brain is often seen as such a complex microcosm within the whole of the universe that we have yet to fully realize its potential and have yet to fully understand it even on a personal level. It is a wonder why there is such little curiosity in the minds of many to more fully investigate the brain's inner workings.

As far as the differences between the two go, the brain is capable of growing literally countless maps aka neural net connections that appear as branches and stem and interlock and cross one another. Yet, if one does not have the mind to grow their own self-perception, or self-knowledge, or intelligence, about one's self and the world, then the mind's consciousness will remain what it is today with little to no growth at all. If this is the case, then little evolves in one's life. This said, many people have heard that the brain has a challenging time retaining information and memory, or learning new things, as we age. While top performers tend to believe that if or when exercised the brain is capable of great things no matter the age of the brain. Something the brain and mind have in common then is that when they are lovingly cared for their functioning can and will develop dramatically.

What do you think improves the functioning of the *mind?*

What do you think improves the functioning of the *brain?*

They have at least one contributor to health in common and that is that meditation helps both of them. Studies show that the mind that meditates is able to have more compassion which in other words translates to tolerance which in turn results in longer lasting relationships with other people as well as longer lasting relationships with one's own biggest and greatest intentions. Another common thread of the mind and brain are that they both benefit from drinking water. In Yoga, water signifies the ability to flow from one posture, or life goal off of the mat, to the next. The brain thrives with the ingestion of water, and includes the increased ability to store memory in the memory banks. The mind will also flow from one thought to the next when the brain is hydrated. In this way, there is an interconnected relationship. Finally, in this brief inquiry, sleep is another factor that the brain, and the mind, have in common as far as how to increase the functioning and optimization of both.

So, then, how are they different?

The mind is connected to the yoga practitioner's stream of consciousness also therefore known as personal consciousness. One's consciousness is really a facet of one's 'higher' self, or as I like to say, 'soul self ', as we might refer to it for now. In Yoga, we aspire to connect with and nourish the part of ourselves that is beyond the physical world as well as treat the body as a meaningful, and valued, part of our existence. The brain will find earthly ways to perform the mind's intentions, goals, dreams, and needs but left to its own devices the brain is just that: an organ that communicates with the body to signal base needs and attain desires.

We as yoga practitioners must have the presence of mind to listen to our brain's signals. However, our minds are called "Monkey

Mind" for a reason. When we sit and listen to our bodies' needs then we set ourselves up for success, and even for optimal communication between the brain and the mind. When we have the presence of mind, or soulful connection, to set intention for our practice then both our inward experience, and our physical yoga practice, will lead practitioners around us to enriched meaning. Now, perhaps if one were to take the mind's involvement out from their practice and merely listen to their body's needs by responding directly to the body's signals then the survivor of trauma might very well excel through their healing process but without a conscious mental narrative that can be revisited off the yoga mat in real life.

Whereas, the often most unrecognized part of healing for any trauma survivor is to allow the body to complete its healing process by closely listening to what the body needs to express, in each moment as a byproduct of the original trauma, without conscious recognition of what's happening, through the redirecting of bodily stories with mental engagement, in the form of writing on paper beside the yoga mat, the mind-body or brain-body union, or yoga, is only half realized. Each trauma really is organic to each survivor's life. The patterning it has left in the body in the form of breath connection restrictions, or muscle contractions, is unique to the survivor. The survivor can *feel* their way to whole life living again through a more free roam expression of yoga practice. Yoga can look a million ways and it is important to honor that within oneself and the practitioners who grace the facilitator's life with their presence.

Unfreezing the Survivor

As a TCY® facilitator you will see one of the ongoing marks of shame and pain in the trauma survivor by way of the limited range of motion observed in the body. One might think the cause is simply "inflexibility". But, the equal if not more truth is that when the body-brain complex holds marks of the past of how the survivor of trauma was often limited in body movement at the time of the traumatic event. In fact, many researchers agree that current day symptoms of Post Traumatic Stress are most prevalent in one's life when the survivor has frozen at the time of the past event. So, what do we do with this knowledge? As TCY® facilitators we become aware that the feelings of stagnancy and restlessness, as if one is unable to make accurate movement and cause and effect within their lives, is a byproduct of a triggered nervous system.

This said, triggered does not always look like annoyance, frustration, or rage. It can and often does appear as a non-willingness to move within one's life. The feeling itself of being stuck is often the byproduct of having a central nervous system that has been triggered and resorted to the felt coping mechanism of non-movement as a form of solution. If one froze during a traumatic event then it is often the case that freezing will appear again and again until one finds the awareness, courage, and willpower to find movement within the body-brain complex's inclination to freeze. Is freezing a weakness? Is the self, 'less than' because one may have frozen as a response to the event? The firm answer is **no.** In fact, the ability to make the choice if one freezes or not is **not** within the conscious reach of the survivor at the time of the event when it mattered most.

The part of the brain that chooses if one will fight, take flight, or freeze is not within reach of the conscious self. There is still much research taking place on an ongoing basis with countless new information, views, and insights formulating every year. It is a fascinating topic that leads to only more discoveries. However, leading doctors do agree that the decision of whether or not the threatened person will fight, take flight, or freeze is not made consciously. In fact, if the threatened person has not had mental, emotional, and/or physical preparation in one's life **BEFORE** the traumatic event takes place then at the time of the event it is believed that a part of the brain renders the experiencer of trauma ill-prepared and shuts down the brain's location that allows the person to physically move. Therefore, you may see now why it is *less* of a conscious choice to surrender, or relent to another's toxic or abusive behavior, but rather a switch in the brain itself that based on one's experiences leading up to the event determines *without conscious consultation* whether or not one will have the option available, and therefore ability, to fight or take flight as defense mechanisms.

The National Institute of Health (NIH) quotes, "Freezing is not a passive state but rather a parasympathetic brake on the motor system, relevant to perception and action preparation." In other words, based on all you've experienced, a part of your brain unbeknownst to your conscious brain will decide whether it can handle what is taking place. Let's give an example: If someone is attacked and dragged into an apartment where the individual is forced to partake in actions against the individual's will, and in the past has yet to experience anything like it, nor has taken any form of martial arts in the past, then the body will collapse, or freeze. The body-brain system has no reference point and at that point will go into freeze mode with the intent of self-preservation, and the hopes that the threat will pass soon. It is that moment that the reptilian brain aka the sense brain will take over.

Without overwhelming you, the reader, it is essential to recognize that when or if this response system, neither negative or positive in and of itself, reenters the survivors' experience, in future days, once removed from the original threat, that the facilities of the frontal lobe part of the brain are often non-functioning, and therefore quite unhelpful in the resolution of traumatic symptoms post-event. This means that the frontal lobe facilities of calculating thought, and planning, go "off the radar" so to speak. As trauma survivors this is how so many hours, days, weeks, months or even years can be lost. The survivor simply disengages from life as it has been known.

The turning point is that with the survivor's growing awareness of the brain functions, and beginning to recognize one's unique bodily responses, as yoga practitioners we are able to re-assign the grief of life lost in our lives to be replaced with what it feels like to become fully alive, again. This is a process and takes time and is not to be rushed or forced by outside influences. As a facilitator it is incredibly important to model the behaviors to attendees of your classes without force or expectation that anyone will be where you are, *or not,* on any given day of practice.

Chapter 4: A Glimpse into The Trauma Survivor's Nervous System

Have you ever seen a photo of a brain that has been affected by life trauma? Here's the situation: the brain is highlighted in all sorts of areas instead of being focused in specific regions. It is the author's experience that this scattered concentration of brain activity not only leads to a difficult time focusing, due to the brain's messages constantly changing, as well as having a sense of agency for oneself, but also leads to states experienced in the body, mind, and emotional self. If you feel like you're never doing one thing, because your brain is quite literally doing more things at once than it had done before the trauma, then this is likely to further create overwhelm, anxiety, and hypervigilance. These are but a few things that the trauma survivor experiences.

If the body's condition reflects itself in the brain's activity as well as in the quality of presence of mind within the survivor then where do we start in order to soothe the central nervous system? In the classroom while facilitating you might mention, "Remember, our bodies are often a mirror of our minds." Then, add in comforting, easy, antidotal, language: "The great news is we're here together now in Yoga class." This statement hones in on mind presencing so as to be free of any excessive mental burdens. "So, let's make conscious decisions throughout practice together of what is needed in each moment as we focus on our body's present needs in each moment." All of that took about 30 seconds to say but makes all the difference in reminding practitioners that we are each stewards of our own bodies.

Developing Awareness of The Triune Brain

In general, as a safe blanket statement, the impact of trauma on the body and brain is the state of experiencing sensory overload. Therefore, it is our job as Trauma Cooperative Yoga® facilitators to invite, encourage, and ultimately accept that people are beginning to sense the world as it is *now* instead of how the trauma *was*. The traumatized body was likely incapable of digesting or integrating the massive load of sensory information that is occurring during a traumatic event. In general, traumatic events are just that because the experiencer of the trauma does not have a reference for the event, and therefore is often under-equipped to respond, and adjust, to the event at hand. This reality is incredibly disempowering, and for many insufferable.

The area of the brain near the occipital base is the brain stem. If you were to do a simple search online of the trauma affected brain, and the unaffected brain, you will notice how the unaffected-by-trauma brain has a high concentration of activity or "energy" lighting up the brain stem area. The brainstem region is responsible for our *sensing* of the world. It is therefore safe to both acknowledge and now say that when we learn to engage in bodily sensing the world, again, in a safe space, as trauma survivors we might possibly begin to heal the brainstem area by increasing activity in that area of the brain once again, too. In reality, yoga is just one big invitation to sense more deeply and widely.

How fascinating is it that we spend most of our time in our thinking and feeling parts of our brains rather than our sensing brain region? It is ironic that although we have learned to rise above animalistic sensing alone, as we have evolved throughout time as homo sapiens, that learning to live again from within this part of the brain is a beneficial component of the survivor's healing. We as people still require of ourselves to be 'sense-makers' as much as we are 'free will navigators of the world.' *Personal meaning,* and the moral of the story, are still required to fulfill our human narratives. As Judith Hermann relentlessly points out in her book, *Trauma and Recovery,* we cannot learn anything until we sense we are safe. Only then may we access those more 'evolved' parts of our brains involving the ability to associate with feeling words, and construct a *mental sense* of a traumatic situation.

The irony is that thought alone does not elevate us above the complex issues of being human although this is one of our favorite go-tos as deep thinkers. It is in fact our ability to newly *sense* the world, then relate to our feelings, and only then may we learn to think about the world in such a way that highlights our ability to both live with the felt *and sensed* realities in a way that allows us to *build a life* post-trauma. Life is constantly evolving and we as people, trauma survivors, and/or facilitators get to decide if we are going to evolve with our life's most recent findings, or not. The work of being a yoga facilitator is one that we are asking people to consistently acknowledge where they are at within their personal self-awareness while requesting that they use that very awareness to continue to provide insight into where they might be able to go next. We always want that direction to be one that is most honoring of the whole self, including physical, mental, and emotional components.

A Health Recovery Awareness Tool: The Vagus Nerve

The vagus nerve exits at the base of the skull, is the largest cranial nerve, and is an integral tool of awareness for your Trauma Cooperative Yoga® facilitation. When the vagus nerve is in a state of dysfunction, possibly due to poor posture, or something as intense as trauma, or a combination of both, it can exacerbate mental and physical conditions that are often already a risk factor for the traumatized body. This includes but is not limited to anxiety, moodiness, gastrointestinal health, and chronic inflammation. As many health practitioners know inflammation itself can lead to heart disease, stroke, and autoimmune disorders such as arthritis, and beyond. This is an extremely long list that might be positively reduced through a regular yoga practice!

The resource ZenFounder.com covers the four vital areas affected by the condition of the vagus nerve. Firstly, it includes the parasympathetic branch of the autonomic nervous system that supplies the internal organs, the blood vessels, stomach, intestines, liver, kidneys, bladder, genitals, lungs, pupils, heart, and sweat, salivary, and digestive glands. Secondly, the sensory part of the body is affected depending on the health state of the vagus nerve. The vagus nerve processes sensory information from the heart, lungs, abdomen and throat. Next, the motor functions of the body are dependent on the vagus nerve as the vagus nerve makes movement to the neck muscles themselves possible, and therefore speech and swallowing readily available. Last but not least, the special sensory of the body works in tandem with the vagus nerve. This means that even the sensation of taste is made to be a known reality for every human being due in part to the function of the vagus nerve.

The most amazing realization that you will find over and over again in your own research of the vagus nerve is that its health is positively influenced by not only engaging and refraining from specific body movements, but also by conjuring healthy thoughts, participating in uplifting healthy social connections, and even learning to breathe in a most natural way to you. Dr Stephen W. Porges writes two books on the subject including The Polyvagal Theory: Neurophysiological Foundations of Emotions, Attachment, Communication, Self Regulation. As well as, The Pocket Guide to Polyvagal Theory: The Transformative Power of Feeling Safe.

How To Increase Healthy Vagal Tone in the Vagus Nerve

There is a growing pile of work that points to yoga helping to regulate the nervous system because of its ability to increase vagal tone making it easier for a practitioner to effectively respond to stress. Yoga practitioners worldwide will factually tell you that their own consistent yoga practice increases their ability to handle and manage stress. However, the research found in scores on the subject only further increases our own self-efficacy and encourages us to become more sensitive toward the trauma survivor needs.

You might visualize the vagus nerve as "the seeker"; it moves throughout the entire body and affects all areas of the body on a regular basis. It's seeking to discover the healthy state or lack thereof within the body as a whole. It's the primary health communicator between the brain and the body as it is the largest cranial nerve as mentioned. The healthier the vagus nerve, or vagal tone, is then the more adept the survivor is at moving from an adversarial triggered state to a positively triggered state where a person's thoughts, actions, and feelings are activated to focus on one's overall wellness. Realistically, we are only capable of influencing the health of "our seeker nerve" if we believe from the get-go that we're capable of doing so. This is self-efficacy at its finest.

Increase and Maintain Healthy Vagus Functioning

In an article, *"How to Stimulate Your Vagus Nerve for Better Mental Health"* as produced by Jordan Fallis with the University of Ottawa we learn of simple and quick ways where you may practice yoga both on and off the mat by merging conscious mental awareness with felt sense physical action. They include but surely are not limited to cold exposure (this includes cold water at the end of your shower for 30 seconds or cold water dips in between sauna visits even); singing or humming, gargling; and the ingestion of probiotics to increase gut health that therefore improves brain function, and positively influences vagal tone. Last but not least, laughing supports a healthy vagal tone. In order to learn them all you might want to visit Jordan Fallis' work online, and beyond.

Vagal Conclusion

In short, the vagus nerve starts at the brainstem and innervates all of the body's organs. This is why in Trauma Cooperative Yoga® you will often hear and want to remind yourself and everyone that it is essential to be mindful not to compress the neck in any of the postures so as not to negatively impact the brainstem functioning. Not only does it reduce the flow of blood and cerebrospinal fluid in the spine, and brain centers, as I have been saying for years in my classes in the USA and Canada, doing so also works against nurturing healthy vagal tone. Since the nerve starts at the neck, with caring awareness you might encourage yourself and practitioners to do as I like to by offering up the gentle remedy, "You might want to turn" or "I am turning" the corners of your/my mouth up as you/I inhale in your/my own time" And, "as you find your own natural timing for your exhale soften the jaw."

Learning to Dance Between 'Amped and Mellow'

In Trauma Cooperative Yoga® as active facilitators we need to recognize that people are served in being both 'amped up' and 'mellow', and no energy is 'too much ' nor 'too little'. The two main states or functions of the autonomic nervous system are the modes of either parasympathetic, or sympathetic. The sympathetic nervous system in this modern day evolution of humans is often overly-sympathetic, or reactive, to both our immediate surroundings and our triggers born from past experiences that show up in the present day. The parasympathetic is a more realized state that is cultivated from within the survivor based on what we take note of and bring to our consciousness recognition through active reflection of our surroundings, and being in this state can soften how we tend to respond to our immediate surroundings. Let's look at this in more detail.

The Sympathetic Nervous System is our most effective tool as human beings to alert us when there is something wrong, or potentially wrong, in our setting or environment. When or if the autonomic nervous system becomes triggered we go into high-alert, fight or flight mode. Our sense is that we need to take massive action immediately in order to preserve our lives. That's a plus, right? Yes, we are often nurtured by this reaction in a high-risk situation. The problem that survivors face is that when this switch gets turned on during the actual traumatic event it's oftentimes difficult to shut off without conscious work on the survivor's part. In some trauma survivors it flat out has been "switched on " for an extended amount of time, and begins to interfere with how the vital organs function and thus how the brain and the mind perceive the world itself. Ironically enough, sometimes the sympathetic nervous system being triggered can result in the body to freeze.

The Parasympathetic Nervous System is known as the rest and digest mode of the body. Meaning, when we are calm and in a state of homeostasis we discover within ourselves a wealth of health.

When we allow ourselves to utilize tools such as the yoga postures, and breathing, we can often intentionally reset our nervous system's state of being into one of wellness and vitality. This is why the practice of yoga is so vital to the trauma survivor. As survivors and/or facilitators of trauma survivors' yoga classes, we need to remember that the parasympathetic nervous system *can be* positively triggered. We may influence our nervous system to shift to parasympathetic by meditating or focusing on feelings, thoughts, physical actions, and the social interactions we choose that yield a pleasurable sense of calm and peace. This said, all feelings, even those that are not considered harmonious, are worthwhile and capable of encouraging healing within any trauma survivor, and can result in parasympathetic activation, when worked mindfully on and off of the mat. It is a matter of being conscious as life runs through us. It is therefore essential to honor, and as a facilitator and teacher *allow and encourage*, all feelings to be present within your Trauma Cooperative Yoga® classroom as outlined in this book.

Parasympathetic Engagement

The parasympathetic rest and digest autonomic nervous system is always within reach. When your heart is pounding, and your breath is only a component of your mental awareness, instead of being an immediately-accessible, and fully-felt, bodily reality, it is by your active choice to reconnect to the present moment in a new felt way that will help you to shift. This takes work, like any other worthwhile task. As tensions arise in our environments, as anxieties or fears explode around us, one way to gain conscious ground over our reactions is to go into the second brain, or the gut, with the breath. It has been said that the gut holds 95% of the body's serotonin.

Therefore, by keeping an active low belly breath, as we did at birth, not only do we create more blood flow to our second brain, but we increase the healthy function and delivery of healthy chemicals to our brain. No matter how stressful an environment is, the way we perceive it, and allow it to run through us, or try to restrict it, and therefore delay its passing, alters our success rate of getting out of it. Our task as yoga practitioners is learning ourselves, including our bodies' felt sensations, enough that we may learn to cope in a way that promotes health long term. The one simple physical marker that we may rely on in order to change the messaging between our gut to our brains, and the resulting mental mindset and moods activated by doing so, is to shift the breath down from the chest.

As we inhale, our low bellies are meant to expand. It makes sense as the stomach region is becoming full of the breath that we are taking in. As we exhale, our navel is meant to tighten inward, and upward, in order to massage the tensions in our bellies. Nevertheless, this one simple act of switching the breath from the chest to the belly, helps to positively trigger the start of our shifting into the parasympathetic nervous system.

Building in More Brain Awareness into Classes

This section is written with great credit to Annie Wilson, published in *Inner Light*, for her amazing in-depth article written on the insula. The idea is for graduates of the Trauma Cooperative Yoga® trainings to understand the areas of the brain that are part of the journey of healing Post Traumatic Stress symptoms within the self so that we may then improvise and collaborate with the power of our imaginations to create exercises for our practitioners that build into their reconstruction of self on the yoga mat. Change can take a number of years, and if we're lucky as seekers of self-development, it is beneficial if the process of returning to life doesn't take away from the years of living it.

In Wilson's article, *Yoga and Meditation for Balancing The Insula of The Brain,* we learn that the root meaning of the word "insula" means "island". We further learn that the insula is incredibly self-sufficient. The word came into use around 1800. So, relatively recently. The insula deals with how we observe the inner sensations of feelings within our bodies. The insula also has some other key responsibilities that are integral to the trauma survivor's wellness and getting back on track after trauma. These are: controlling personal emotions, regulating the overall health or homeostasis of the body. The term homeostasis means, on a physiological level, the ability of a living organism to adjust its internal environment to maintain a state of dynamic constancy. These include body temperature, and blood sugar levels.

The National Center for Biotechnology Information states,"Traumatic events disrupt homeostasis in multiple areas of the brain that are recruited to respond to the threat." Therefore, it is vital that we cover the role of the insula in this book and on the mat. The insula is responsible for communication between the body and the brain and therefore influences the mind, too. The insula serves to scan the body. An article in *Nature* suggests that it is a crucial link between cardiac interoception and anxiety levels and depending on its health can improve self-regulation. This is huge in the mind-body/body-brain negotiation of how trauma will affect one's life after the fact.

Yoga and meditation have now been proven to increase the healthy matter of the brain as well as the efficiency and abilities of the insula. In this same publication, *Nature,* the insula is noted to play a pivotal role in the integration and representation of how the sensory signals perceive the physiological state of the body. Knowing that practicing yoga increases the health of the insula, means that the communication between brain and the messengers of the body is greatly improved for the total and long lasting health of the survivor.

Chapter 5: Cultivating Healthy Power Dynamics in the Classroom

How to Encourage Self-Efficacy on the Mat

The cornerstones or 'sources' of self-efficacy as defined by Albert Bandura in his PositivePsychology.com publication are listed as such:

- Mastery experiences
- Vicarious experiences
- Verbal persuasion
- Emotional and physiological states (Akhtar, 2008).

In so many words, mastery experiences are moments in our lives that resulted in perceived positive outcomes as assessed by the person living the experiences. In Trauma Cooperative Yoga® as facilitators we want to take this information on board with the idea in mind to affirm when someone comes to you and says they enjoyed the practice. As a facilitator you might say, "Thank you." And, "That is great that you made so much of the practice today." Or, simply, "You made it happen." "I'm glad you enjoyed so much of your practice today." Of course, from a business end, you might say, "We love having you here every time, ________(practitioner's name)." This recentering on the effort of the practitioner-in-attendance is to further reinforce that it is because of both the collective, *and the inward,* experience that everyone is rewarded, and gains positive experience.

Secondly, vicarious experience, as noted by the Istanbul graduate, Uyanga Tugsbaatar, in the *Positive Psychology* article, refers to having enriching role models whose successful behaviors are observed, and likely carried out through the observer in her or his future. As a yoga facilitator you might consider thinking about the full gamut of life experiences that the survivor before you has, and therefore your own ability to reinforce present moment awareness, or presence making, and healthy self-relations. The language we use, and the references we might refrain from using, all matter and affect whether someone is able to center themselves in the present moment, or not. The traditional way a practitioner relates to a teacher is to deify them, or exalt them as sage beings. Many practitioners come to a class and choose a teacher with the idea that they are learning from a perfect or enlightened being. This viewpoint is deleterious. In order to perceive oneself as having the internally-born ability to self-affect one's course of action and succeed, both on or off the yoga mat, aka self-efficacy, we must refrain from the mindset of exalting another or placing the existence of another, as the ultimate goal for oneself.

Admittedly, as the powerful beings we are in the position of guide, teacher, and facilitator, *if* we start with our own experience throughout the class it is a marker of our shared humanness and we give those practicing alongside us greater access to their own self-reference through our own courage to start the conversation. The yoga mat is a great reminder for people to listen to their own innate wisdom, and that they needn't live through our own strides in order to succeed in their lives on their yoga mats. Just because we as facilitators have figured out a new way to touch our toes, does not mean that they need to jump on that train and start doing the same thing.

When we reflect long enough we might discover that it is a reality that many people are coming to class 'to be spiritually saved', although they might not speak those words, or to be temporarily removed from their life's hardships. Rather than encouraging escapism, as facilitators, the invitation is to recenter ourselves first with short factual statements about why we're making the body-based, *and at times the mental-emotional-based decisions,* that we are practicing on the mat. Then, from there, constantly reminding the practitioners to best choose their own course of action in relationship to their own full selves. In traditional yoga, we practice the physical to connect and unite with the mental self with more clarity, in order to bring more self-knowledge, and to connect with more resolution to the emotional and spiritual parts of self through practice. In TCY® we propose the open engagement of connection with all parts of self in order to further the practice of wholeness. The practice becomes an open discussion of transparency, without hiding, or keeping to one's self, parts of the whole.

Moving forward, the next cornerstone of self-efficacy as described by Tugsbaatar Bandura is verbal persuasion, which is simply how our words affect ourselves and people. As you may recall, it is now known that our social connections affect the ability for a person to have a healthy vagal tone, or not. The book, *Originals* by Adam Grant, talks about the impact of words on people and how people who are spoken to in an encouraging way have been shown within case studies to perform much higher than people who are directed under a person who is negative toward them. Therefore, perhaps in addition to you as a yoga practitioner and facilitator thinking about how words impact your practitioners you might also consider teaching what healthy self-affirmation can potentially look like in both your solo, self-directed, and shared classes. Please refer to this book, *Conquer Trauma Drama: Get Your Life Back,* about ways to phrase verbal reinforcements both to self and beyond.

Finally, within the context of Bandura's work, emotional and physiological states are mentioned as covered by Tugsbaatar in the aforementioned *Positive Psychology* article. This area of exploration is instrumental in the exploration of creating an inner environment that is conducive for healthy vagal tone because an element of healthy vagal tone is feeling the healthier feelings that are available to us. In the event that the body is experiencing ease, rest, and pleasure then the 'brain-body', more on this concept later in the book, will not only produce healthy chemicals that feed the mind to create healthy thoughts but also will build into conscious mental wellness to take place. The peaceful emotions, and mental attitudes, are then locatable in the body itself. Following, the body's lack of constriction and tension will give space for the health of the vagal tone in the body to improve. In Trauma Cooperative Yoga® we really are focusing on the whole sense of what it means to embrace and embody the true meaning of yoga-union.

Co-Creative Class Ideas

So far, we've learned about how trauma survivors must be active co-participants on a regular basis in order to become, and maintain, self-empowered in the mat-based trauma resolution process. We have very briefly touched on many of the philosophical and structural differences of a Trauma Cooperative Yoga® class.

Here is one idea for you as a practitioner of yoga as well as a potential guide for others:

1. Place a white board and dry erase markers at the front of the room that will be visible for all yoga practitioners in your classroom. Encourage practitioners to write two positive side effects they want from the class on that practice day. You might include that it is helpful if they write one body-based intention, and one mind-based intention, for the class. Here are some examples of intentions for growth outcomes to get you started...

Mind-Based Examples:

"I center my focus to return to my breath throughout class today."

"I feel joy at least once in my practice today."

"I allow myself to confidently move from one posture to another while checking-in with myself frequently."

"I accept myself and my limitations whether they be temporary or permanent."

"I seek approval from myself first and foremost."

Body-Based Examples:

"My hips feel more open today."

"My energy levels are steady throughout the class today."

"When I notice myself smiling at times, I allow myself to smile wider."

"My shoulders are more open today."

"I embrace shaking as part of the process of becoming strong in my postures."

You might even photocopy this page to share with yourself and practitioners in future classes. If you plan on implementing this it is key to show up to class 30 minutes from the time of class start time and tell practitioners that the door will be unlocked 15 minutes before class starts. This gives you time to warm up the space with candles, or lightly tidy up or clean, and get yourself warmed up if you like to practice a few minutes of meditation or postures before sharing the practice with your attendees. It also gives them a chance to write on the proposed whiteboard as they may wish to do.

Give Practitioners Your Best

Realize that people when triggered, depressed, or numb often lose a working connection to an effectively functioning frontal lobe. As you may recall, this is the area behind the forehead that governs conscious thought. If or when a yoga practitioner is affected by one's trauma as one is practicing on the mat then it might be difficult to regain one's equilibrium as quickly as one might if a proactive observer is present to offer constructive "you might" options that possibly pertain to them, and their needs, and/or liking. In the event of this "frontal lobe interruption", it can make it a real challenge to maintain traction with one's intentions as the intentions have been set out to be at the start of class. Therefore, if you have a laminated poster or large piece of paper at the front of the room that is easily visible you might want to have the acronym, **M.A.T.** written on it with the meaning of each letter, as learned in the previous pages earlier on in this book.

Note to the Reader of This Book: The reality is that even when we've been practicing Yoga for years when under extreme stress we might lose our center. This applies especially to those people who have high paced lifestyles outside of their Yoga practice. The body is a powerful recording device. It remembers the state of being that you most often live within. *Then, it repeats it back to you, and sometimes at inopportune times.* That's why getting your body to experience new ways of sensing and being is crucial and astronomically vital both in the short term, and long term, for the well-being of the survivor.

Furthermore, when in shock the body gets stuck. When we begin to move around in our day to day lives again the body will, without our conscious pre-frontal lobe knowing, or any conscious mental execution, be looking to return to a "place of comfort". It will therefore seek out the pattern that it was in at the time of preserving itself during the trauma. The central problem with this is that "freezing" was not indefinitely what saved the survivor of trauma. That was and is simply a mode that the body chooses to go into when the sensory nervous system is overwhelmed, and doesn't know what else to do. And, all without any conscious mental conversation, or self-dialogue, within the mind of the survivor. As survivors the best and most empowering thing we can do is remind ourselves over and over that freezing in immobility, after the initial threat has passed, is an outdated response system to a menace that is no longer present. This takes extreme willpower.

As Trauma Cooperative Yoga® facilitators, it is the crux of our integral value as facilitators to make it easier on the survivor to return to themselves and their lives one breath at a time.

How to Encourage Self-Agency in Practitioners

In the life of a trauma survivor *with unresolved trauma*, the survivor who observes their life often recognizes very little freedom to be had. As a byproduct, solutions are seemingly missing. This said, nothing is ever beyond the power of any trauma survivor. Every human being can shift beyond their current day's challenges, no matter how large or small, if the survivor feels the ability to resolve matters. Therefore, the survivor's action to embrace yoga even for one class is a momentous step in the right direction. It is our job as Trauma Cooperative Yoga® facilitators to continue encouraging the human souls in our class to make those self-directed steps toward their *own* solutions.

Now, we all need support, and inspiration, as well as encouragement from people no matter who we are, or how much of our 'stuff' we have together. This said, as facilitators we need to understand the ways to encourage self-agency. This emphasis was further inspired when I was approached by a trainee with the following feedback. The note talked about a person who had lost someone near and dear to them and felt shaken by a song that came on in a yoga class that this particular Trauma Cooperative Yoga® trainee was teaching.

It read like this,

"...Of course, I didn't know the song would trigger a response but what do you say when the practitioner engages you about it? I want to be sensitive and acknowledge that the practitioner is sharing something very personal. Do you offer comfort? Like you said, they aren't looking for 'advice' so much as they are sharing in the name of their own rehabilitation process. I like your tips on verbiage in these training sessions. Please advise!" - TCY® trainee

So, as we see the main focus is "If I do, *how* do I offer comfort?" The trainee also talks about the fact that people are looking to share their experiences as part of their own rehabilitation post-trauma. Although we want people to share their experiences as a way to free minds, hearts, souls, and bodies of their residue, it is key that we stay within our scope of practice as facilitators. As a yoga facilitator, one *might* choose to educate in professional coaching, counseling, social work, and/or psychology, or any number of holistic approaches that compliment yoga as a way to further be of support.

If one *chooses* to do this it is an admirable commitment to make to one's community. However, if one loves and is devoted to their primary role as yoga teacher and facilitator then perhaps the best answer to this question is how do you want to offer support? Is your studio a place where people have tea or fresh-squeezed juice afterward? If yes, then provide a listening ear while responding to any questions they might have of you with the knowledge that whereas you enjoy holding space for them, you're confident that they don't need advice from you because they have the answer within. You might say, "I like to give myself time to know answers, because sometimes it takes me awhile to figure out what it is I really need in each moment.So, maybe that's the same for you, too."

A Trauma Cooperative Yoga® Exercise to Encourage Ongoing Self-Agency:

This trainee's question and feedback were invaluable in crafting a yet clearer picture of how to best serve our yoga practitioners in the classroom. They trust us to keep them on course with their personal yoga practice, and sometimes that means giving homework to practitioners to practice. This is especially true when it is homework that is universally helpful. In everyone's case, a key part in healing our personal life's traumas is integration, integration, and more integration.

As trauma survivors, on a journey to heal and whole, we need to be willing and able to touch in with our pains and our joys. As a trauma survivor who was once new to yoga myself, I know the embarrassment of crying in a class only to have people look at you with bewilderment as to why you're crying in the first place. The integration component is the ability to be present in our highs and lows instead of numbing out, or running away. When we as facilitators do our own work to sit with the shame, or embarrassment, of the harder emotions that might, and very often do, arrive in a yoga class, it is easier for the practitioners who choose to be with us in class to also do the same.

When someone chooses to come to your class it is for a reason, season, or lifetime. No matter if they stay for a part of the class, the whole class, or countless classes to come, they chose *you* to be their guide. In the minds of the practitioner, the lines can and often do get blurred when it comes to your role and your purpose as their facilitator. You are a pillar of strength and therefore they very likely will come to you for additional support if you offer more services such as Reiki, massage therapy, craniosacral therapy... or you name it! On the other hand, if you are a health and wellness facilitator who is presently strictly dedicated to yoga, and yoga only, then you might want to try the following suggestion.

Beginning Exercise:

Scenario: a practitioner comes up to you before or after class and divulges that something in that class, or a prior class, has triggered them and made them think so much of their past friend/lover/partner/family member that they'd like to know if there's anything they can do to help stay calm, or present, in their current stage of healing, or experience. Of course, they might not have the realization, or clarity, to use these exact words but if a practitioner is telling you they are re-experiencing something negative, like the client did for the TCY trainee® with the question we just touched on, then it's helpful to come through with some supportive words. **Intimate advice-giving is outside of scope of practice.** However, if you want to share that *you* practice this yoga exercise when dealing with harder emotions and situations then it is their choice to practice the exercise, or not.

ASK: What pose that you've practiced in this class, or another class, might help you express how you are feeling right now/at the time of experiencing what it is that you're describing to me? Wait for them to show you their chosen posture. Then, ask them to stay there and breathe into it for 3-5 breaths.

NEXT: Now, say, "if you were to resolve, or further come to peace with this experience that you've been describing to me, what posture might help express how you might feel in your body?" Wait for them to show you their chosen posture. Ask them to stay there and breathe into it for 3-5 breaths.

FINALLY: Ask the practitioner to write down the two postures they've chosen to express the depth of the challenge they've been experiencing that was, in this case, triggered in class. This action on the practitioner's part will prompt openness and receptivity to the experience of further self-initiated healing and resolution. Suggest that they might benefit from practicing the two postures in the same order *that they just have with you* at home before bed. Make sure to reinforce, "Only if you think it's beneficial to you, and are interested, then you might want to try this at home."

FURTHER CLARITY OR PRACTITIONER DIRECTION: That might be enough for the yoga practitioner in your class in order to feel satisfied that they have an idea of how to self-soothe and self-regulate from home. However, if they are eager to hear more, and only if they ask if there's anything more to that, then as the last part of this you may want to suggest the following:

"For the first week before bed it might benefit to practice your two chosen postures for 10 breaths each. Then, on week two reduce the breaths per posture so that it's 5 breaths per each of the postures. Practice the postures back-to-back one time each. On week three, you might want to practice flowing between the postures for 2 breaths each with a total of 5 rounds."

You might also describe that this is a yoga practice to bring home to highlight the ability to be with the full range of feelings and body sensations and then alternate more fluidly between the two opposites in order to further establish more succinct self-mastery. The purposeful visiting of both extremes within the self, as one has designed and chosen to do on their own, therefore further encourages self-contact and self-knowledge while building strength and personal confidence in the self...not to mention serves to activate greater self-agency.

Increasing Self-Agency with Trauma Cooperative Yoga®

The underscoring of all of humanity's successes is the ability to act with self-agency. The more self-agency is looked upon as valuable in the practice of yoga the more one is able to become conscious of and grow the benefits of yoga throughout one's day as a whole. This awareness of one's ability to act for oneself serves to increase one's dedication to the practice of yoga itself and fully living one's life. The *National Institutes of Health* quotes James W. Moore in his following contribution to the topic of self-agency, "Those working on this may struggle to articulate the relevance and potential impact of what they do." Following this he shares that having agency of self is quite difficult to measure in studies because sometimes people can feel agency without being completely aware of the fact that they are enacting a sense of agency within the self. This is because only sometimes is there conscious thought attached to actions that require self-agency. Meaning, we can take significant action without having any mental self-knowledge about it. We can have drastic shifts in our lives *first* in the body-self, the body that makes it possible to move our lives into action, and the narrative, or mental constructs around that narrative, becomes a conscious part of our lives as a close second.

The awakening to our positive personal power, and ability to self-create the lives that we want, often comes in that order.

TCY® believes that instilling a great awareness of self-agency in the conscious forefront of the brain, known as the thinking mind, is instrumental in developing a greater bodily sense of self that permits knowledge of one's own abilities to self-create, and self-alter, one's thoughts, actions, habits, and ultimately behaviors and responses to life off of the mat. Furthermore, it is natural for people to misplace the center of power even when one's actions are knowingly creating change. Yet, in the event that one perceives *someone else* to be the cause of the change the sense of self-agency can be and often is temporarily or permanently abandoned. For a trauma survivor this first and foremost is a conflicting issue for the sufficient recovery of the survivor both in short and long term. The author of this book has taught for nearly two decades and personally experienced yoga practitioners coming up to her and applauding her for the great work they themselves had actually done in the class. Sometimes this looked like practitioners thanking her for having said something of a poignant nature when she had in fact said something of the very nature yet an early stage of conception as far as thoughts go. The reality was that the practitioner had deduced their own knowledge from what she had said as a facilitator and then tried to give that triumph of having done so to her.

In the realm of creating self-agency, and becoming a master or director of one's own life, it is essential to recognize the productivity, effectiveness, and even brilliance of one's own thinking. TCY® encourages practitioners to track their thoughts and even notate them if within a resting posture, or seated, as a means to cultivate greater self-understanding, or 'innerstanding', as the author likes to say. In so doing, one recognizes their own doing in representing themselves and their own unique evolution on the yoga mat. Yoga gives new life to the practitioner who takes time to anchor oneself within their own inner knowing and allow that sense of knowing to grow yet greater. Let it be the reality then that facilitators honor this progressive self-knowing within self and in the practitioners before them, and continue to create avenues in class for the expression of self-agency.

Calling Oneself to Awaken

In the book *Siddhartha* the words are written, "He pondered about this sensation, which filled him completely, as he was slowly walking along. He pondered deeply, like diving into a deep water he let himself sink down to the ground of the sensation, down to the place where the causes lie, because to identify the causes, so it seemed to him, is the very essence of thinking, and by this alone sensations turn into realizations and are not lost, but become entities and start to emit like rays of light what is inside of them." Jo shares, "I spent many years following exact instructions on the yoga mat to the best of my ability and sometimes too much in order to actively listen to what was being asked of me and the room in a bodily sense." The meeting of the enthusiastic suggestions of the teachers brought a sense of accomplishment to her. In other words, she felt fulfillment in having succeeded in something although the design of the class was not hers to begin with nor were her inner signals responded to fully. Instead, the listening of bodily messages were present only within the confines of the assigned yoga postures. Never did she venture outside of what was being asked of her in order to discover on her own. In fact, that might have had something to do with her initial yoga teacher training leader having an issue with her closing her eyes in a warrior one. She did so for the sake of possibly activating her sense of bodily feeling that can be overrun by the visual and smelling senses. She wanted to feel her feet touching the floor more, and grow her roots deeper. The offense taken by the lead trainer that day not only brought about a sense of embarrassment for her being called out on the mat but added a layer of shame for not being more of what was being asked of her by her instructing teacher.

Her energy began to be depleted when the said ritual of following instructions began to become too much an inner indicator of her personal capability, or lack thereof, as a person of value and worthiness. In this noticing of misdirected self-attainment through the over emphasis of meeting people's expectations, or suggestions, of her she began to shift on the mat first. Instead, she began to listen inwardly even if it meant possibly offending the instructor before her. This crafted her ability to see more deeply into what her body needed. As a byproduct of this new approach, she was able to introduce more ideas of honest substance to the practitioners who showed up to her yoga class week after week.

The yoga practitioners in her classes became intrigued as were the yoga studio owners who ventured to support such spontaneous though necessary self-study. Although attendees of her classes were happy, over time she began to meet opposition from teachers whose classes she attended. One, upon her stretching into her hip by introducing small circular movements into her low pelvis from downward facing dog, called out across the classroom for her to, in his words, "stop shaking her hips." This took place in the one of the most prominent yoga meccas in the world of Vancouver, Canada at an equally prestigious yoga studio.

It became clear that there was or is a bias in movement when it comes to what is supported on the yoga mat, and what is not. In that moment of time she was not in harm's way, nor was she at risk of harming herself or anyone else. In that particular moment, she was stretching into her lumbar spine and easing latent energy that had rooted itself there during one of her late into the evening writing marathons. Yet, the restriction placed on her bodily movement was there nonetheless. It became apparent that change was needed, and that this change would need to come from heightened self-study efforts, the study of her own practice, and of the lineage of yoga. Perhaps, this might lead to where the restriction lay and even why the man at the front of the room trained in power vinyasa had felt the urgent need to correct the micromovement, in the first place. After many days, weeks, months, and years of this study this book has come into play. It is written as a look toward what is possible if we remove some of the self-limitations placed by eons of years of self-complacency stewarded by fears of standing out, being oneself, and of seeking to resolve one's own disadvantageous approaches to life as life moves through the body itself and manifests what it does. Inwardly and outwardly one's transformation and independent resolution occurs because of one's willingness to honestly look at what one is feeling and what one is ready to do about it.

Let's Go Deeper

Although yoga can positively trigger the rest and digest mode of the autonomic nervous system, if someone is highly-traumatized it might just put the stress response of fight, flight, or freeze in action. The difference in how effective yoga is for reorienting the trauma survivor's nervous system toward the rest and digest branch of the autonomic system is whether or not the practitioner, who is a trauma survivor learning to listen to needs, is either knowingly or unknowingly practicing self-agency. Therefore, there are noticeable markers, and moments designated in Trauma Cooperative Yoga®, that give way to this recognition of self-needs. Before we venture toward a few possible exercises that the TCY® practitioner may employ in their practice on the mat, let's delve deeper into how the author came to recognize in her own life the need for this self-efficacy of a more self-directed practice.

Although the practice was influential in the author's life by developing greater focus and physical stamina, as well as participating in and forming communities, she began to realize the need for the practice of personal wherewithal in the flow of the practice. Afterall, in the desire to do what is suggested by the instructor-teacher, as meticulously as possible, there is an element of self-connection that is lost. Therefore, self-reference throughout yoga, in relation to what one is needing at that present moment, is instrumental in reforming the opinion of self that one is able to center action around what caters to one's present moment wellness.

This new lens of self starts first on the mat and then onward. In this more nuanced approach the practitioner figures out what detracts and adds to the experience of consciously building one's new sense of self.

Although the author had grown the ability to follow instructions she didn't know how to listen effectively so that the same sense of wellness could carry over to all areas of her life. Furthermore, on the traditional yoga mat she was often aware of an overactive nervous system that was fueled by the realization of her inability to practice with more self-appointed agency. For study reference, the author had endured multiple big-T traumas before beginning her vocation of practicing and teaching. It was after her own yoga trainings that she came to know more of the latent power in herself, only it was perceived by her to be relevant in the limited capacity of being able to lead others. The ability to lead herself toward higher ground in her own personal life eluded her. The realization of her being able to make great change possible rarely carried over to her own life.

The presence of mind she came to know in her home yoga practice, and in teaching others practitioners, was so different from the "regular" or "normal" state of mind that she operated from *when not on her mat.* The positive sense of personal power that she felt when moving the yoga practitioners in her classroom toward their own greatness on the mat was not being carried over to her own "mat of life". Despite the sense of excitement and connection that occurred in the moments of yoga flow it was rare for her to feel such power or the ability to positively impact her own personal life. No matter how great she became in the lives of others her own sense of self-agency and self-growth off the mat was stymied by lacking the sense of having any lasting command over her own life. She knew it was time to rewrite her relationship with the alliance that had most impacted her life: yoga practice.

But, where to begin?

She wanted to stay a yoga teacher to the public yet knew that both her relationship to yoga and her relationship to self needed to shift. She knew it was going to look different than how she had come to be told to practice. And, she knew her own life very much so needed to change in order to incite this kind of a shift in her own sacred, and much-relied upon yoga practice, that had been her glue for her own trauma recovery. Or, at least to the extent in which she had healed up until that point. Choice wasn't an option in her trauma just as it is not present for so many in traumas that involve irrational violence that does not defend the pulse of life, heart, soul, or kin.

It's not that heinous crimes were committed or improprieties were alive. It's that she didn't feel she had a choice to end relationships that needed to be ended in the time that they needed to come to an end. Or, that she could give just as much love to herself that she gave to others. Likewise, that her worth was enough that she deserved to have people around her who supported her in all her fullness no matter what, and with the knowledge that if they didn't she could forge new bonds. In short, she lacked self-agency. Despite being able to conjure up extensive class plans that met many of the needs of the practitioners showing up in her class she was at a loss as to how to create an inner self that bolstered her outward projections of being able to do great things in life.

In order to get her nervous system to anchor in rest and digest she needed to listen more deeply. She needed permission to meander along on her path on the mat. It was in this way that she'd be able to reprogram herself to make this accessibility to self, and self-needs, transferable off of the yoga mat. In order to command herself off of the mat in every life area she needed to know she could steer, rock, shake, circle herself within the posture any way she knew how while staying mindful to the dynamics of the posture, and safety procedures. Since yoga was her mainstay and chosen learning source that she returned to time and time again it was on the mat that she would reorient herself to acclimate to her own inner needs. Then, and only then would self-agency become more of a fixture in her life as well as self-determination *that commingles with one's relationship to agency itself.*

Where to Start

When one's practice on the yoga mat communicates that it's okay to engage with mental flexibility as often as possible, and that it is in fact healthy, then one navigates closer to other nearer and greater truths about self. It is okay if not necessary to engage with one's trauma, it's effects, it's ripples, whisperings, and even seismic shifts. Just as mother nature gives warnings before change is about to occur, so does the human body, mind, and emotional self. If we are honest enough to listen to the change in direction toward an unpleasant or seemingly unbearable inner self, or outer physical self change, and be aware of the ability to welcome, and rock and root, into the sensation then we are at a sensorial advantage. As practitioners and facilitators becoming anticipatory of what one requires moment to moment can significantly change the unfolding of the experience in mat or in life. This remains to be true whether the class is preplanned, or not.

The common issue for trauma survivors is that dissociation occurs where one is disconnected from the present moment, as well as one's inner self-experience. In this case, yoga becomes just another distraction or goal rather than an anchor into the evolution and eventual possibility of self-mastery. Remember, yoga is meant to teach the practitioner about oneself and to liberate oneself from over-embellishment into the negative or non-conducive parts of self. We learn cleanliness of mind, and greater self-awareness, so that we may become less bound by life's pitfalls. In the practice of yoga, we learn to train ourselves that we are far from the negative thought or experience that is occurring. This is **not** because we learn to bypass *or ignore* the feeling or sense but because we resolve to continue on with our practice instead of becoming heavy or immovable with the effects of our trauma.

In trauma, the brain centers stop working in tandem with one another. Rather, they gravitate toward over usage in areas of the brain, or operate in cyclical patterns, with the attempt to focus on and solve the initial disruption in the brain. Whereas there is no way to technically solve something that is no longer actually happening in one's present day experience, the brain requires the ability to opt out of the current way of functioning by garnering the elements of self-options, through willfully building self-agency, and self-determination on the mat. It is therefore essential that the facilitator support the practitioners on the yoga mat to navigate toward more chances to discern one's own needs, and directions, while keeping safety in mind. The affirmation is, "If your body knows it and your body is comfortable with it then practice it. Otherwise, wait until you know more about it before going there." The use of any of the languaging techniques that are outlined in this book, as well as approaches to self-agency, self-communication, and containment of self, all apply in solution making on the mat.

Once again, whereas the brain and the mind are indeed two different parts of the composition of a human life they influence one another and have an interdependent relationship. The mind is impacted by the traumatic changes within the brain due to whatever trauma event has transpired. For example, if a region of the brain is injured then other parts of the brain will have to compensate for the lacking vitality in that area whether it is temporary or stated to be otherwise. This change in the brain will likely modify the activity within the survivor's mind. However, the mind is capable of focusing, through meditation, and through meditatively-engaged, and presenced, body movement. Thereby, the returning to proactively healthy mental exercises can and often will support the rekindling of areas of the brain and contribute to an overall healthy brain once again. This concentration on reorientation to the self can support to re-sense the moment in newly safe, and secure ways.

Options to self-care need to be present, **not** out of required suggestion in relation to beginner, intermediate, advanced options *but as a means to signify the evolution of one's relationship to their practice.* **What is needed to more firmly root the practitioner into the moment?** How might the facilitator compromise one's idea of a "great class plan" with the balanced offering up of various directions that are safe and effective for engaging the practitioner's willful impetus to modify in accordance with one's needs? These are all questions that the work of TCY® seeks and effectively employs answers to for the practitioner in all of us.

SELF-AGENCY EXERCISE: RECOVERING FROM CONFUSION, DISCONNECT, OR OVERWHELM

STEP 1: place hand on the forehead and say, "I notice."

STEP 2: place hands on sides of head in a comfortable hand position and say, "I am feeling."

STEP 3: place hands along the bottom of the back of the head where it connects to the neck and say, "I am sensing."

STEP 4: hands on knees or tops of legs and say, "I am here." And/or, "I am ready to process."

Pause for a moment and notice your natural breath for anywhere from ten seconds to ten minutes. If you haven't already please get a stopwatch or use the free timer in your smartphone to set it for as long as ten minutes. This ensures that you return to the next step of your practice after completing your self-assigned pause length. The intention is to stay committed and connected to a sense of flow and continuation of practice. The resolve to move forward counts in yoga practice, too. Think of the yoga mat as a small world, or sounding board, for what it is you want to create and how you want to act in your life at large.

Scientific Note: It is normal to disconnect from time to time. In fact, Bruce Goldman, in an article in the Stanford Medicine Newsletter, says that, "between 2% and 10% of the population will experience the mysterious phenomenon known as dissociation during their lifetimes," said Karl Deisseroth, MD, PhD, professor of bioengineering and of psychiatry and behavioral sciences, as well as a Howard Hughes Medical Institute investigator. Deisseroth also says that, "Dissociation," which we call disconnection for simple terms, or plain speak, on the yoga mat, "is a phenomenon in which people can feel disconnected from their bodies and from reality." We can see why this is something we want to reduce the chances of happening on the physically-inhabited yoga mat.

STEP 5: Now, let's revisit the original four steps although this time as we cycle through let's do so with greater detail. Cycle through this again, "I notice, I am feeling, I am sensing", and, "I am here/I am ready to process." with the already outlined hand positions. This repetition helps the practitioner to more deeply center and ground into this practice exercise because next we are labeling what is being noticed, felt and sensed as a collective whole.

Practice it like this, "I am noticing__________, I am feeling__________, I am sensing ______________ in my ______________. I now welcome ease in this area by practicing ______________.

STEP 6: Now, physically practice the body movement written down in the last open blank space in step 5.

STEP 7: Repeat steps 1-4 only this time the verbal statement at the end of 4 is **"I am ready to move forward."**

Practice note: if you are desiring to repeat steps 1-7 again and are in a physical classroom or following along to a practice video that you've paused, while practicing this self-recovery exercise, then please do so. Otherwise, reconnect to what's happening in the class, whether virtual or live, and join back into the class at a time that is desirable, safe, and comfortable for you to do so.

If you need to rest then please choose between the resting postures of carefully laying on your back, or seated upright in a comfortable manner. Be sure to use pillows, blocks, blankets, or anything else to assist you. Unlike traditional vinyasa or hatha classes, Downward Facing Dog is not relied upon each time one is invited to "have a rest". This is because in highly-traumatized people you're working with body systems that are already over stressed. So, even positive stress can turn into negative stress. Although there is strength-sourced stress that the practitioner intentionally places on the body, such as in yoga postures, there is the negative type of stress that has been outlined in this body of work. This kind of stress is the involuntary triggering of the body's stress systems that in turns affects the functioning of the body in such a way that builds into overall health. High amounts of cortisol being released into the body, in response to the amygdala aka alarm system of the body being sounded off, due to a misread of current circumstances, or haphazard triggers, is the last thing that we want. We needn't push the body to it's limits.

The last thing we want to do is stress the processing and healing body systems anymore than it is with toxic ideas of strength, and strength-building. The body needs to have the mind to pause or move. This self-tolerance of what-is in the present moment is, in and of itself, a strength. Toxic strength building is the notion that strength has a timeline or projected time frame in which it needs to be expressed in ways that are externally judged by another to be met by. A prime example of this is a "yoga guru" sitting on someone's back in order to step up the timeline for the practitioner to express the strength of flexibility. The practitioner needs to be schooled in self-listening well enough that the art of self-agency may begin to take root and flourish in the first place.

Strength-sourced stress from within is the only stress that benefits the otherwise highly environmentally stressed body of the traumatized person. One way to interpret stress placed on the body is if the demand to move the body any one way or another is made by an *external or internal* driven source. If the demand to move is made by the enthusiastic requests, or suggestions, of a well-intended instructor, rather than through self-initiated focus on sensing, it can often create a sense of disconnect from the present moment, and resultantly one's personal power, as well as a lack of connection to one's own agency. Self-initiated movement is founded on the experience within the body. It is believed in TCY® that it requires inherent strength to address what's already stored within the body. Therefore, toxic ideas of strength have no place on the TCY® mat. Strength is dynamic, and requires we call upon both inner and outer processes.

SELF-AGENCY EXERCISE: CREATING CHANGE/DESIGNATING DIRECTION IN THE BODY

Step 1: Write down the following words, "I feel at ease in my ___________." (for example, tailbone) I welcome this ease by practicing **self-soothing** in this area to bring yet more of a sense of this ease to my body by **assign action**." (for example, doing finger presses on either side of the tailbone on the buttocks.)

Now, practice the finger presses, or the holding of fingers in that area, or whatever is self-soothing for you. Practice this until you feel yet a greater sense of calm or relaxation.

Step 2: Write down the following words, "I notice I am desiring more ease in my ________. (for example, neck.) I welcome this ease by practicing ______________. (write down the posture or self-soothing technique you'd like to do for yourself through self-connection in any way that feels right. For example: ...by practicing self-soothing with firm hand drags along the side of my neck.)

As a facilitator you might be wondering what's next from here. What can you bring forward to the class to work on next that compliments past postures in this flow whilst honoring any sporadic material that comes up in the moment? Remember TCY® is about honoring the inner process. Not, just following the pre-planned flow you've mapped out for the class that was self-prescribed before entering onto the mat or is an ancient series precalculated by people who endured an entirely different culture, ergonomic reality, and while living in an entirely different environment with extremely contrasting requirements of daily life than one has today. The level of informational content absorbed in daily life has increased manifold since the origination of yoga. If we believe the mind and body are one then that fact alone creates an overload of sensory and extra-sensory information. It's difficult for one to come into contact with, and reach oneness with, the innermost self, *who in turn programs our most fulfilling destiny and life,* if we are on overload with external stimuli, and never have self-initiated pauses from what we have planned, or has been planned for us in our day-to-day lives.

Practice Prompts

This practice can feel scary and even self-indulgent but being self-indulgent is necessary sometimes in order to fully learn and 'know thyself.' Here are some ideas to provide the practitioners in your class with and to use in your own practice if or when you feel called to follow them. On a piece of paper you might type these out or ask the class to write down the following **practice prompts** at the start of class. These might support yourself and others to set intentions more skillfully, with mind-presencing, recentering when required, and maintaining one's focus. Really, they can be done sporadically as well as suggested to others to do them throughout class, too.

- I need to ______________________ today. (example: build strength/flexibility/calm down.) This looks like _______________ for me today. (the way we might witness the building of these qualities might be inward or outward in nature. For example: more resting postures, or taking time to slow down enough to notice when something different is happening and/or needed for the practitioner.)
- The areas of my body I need to focus on today are _______________. (**note:** it is important the practitioner decide what areas of the body are to be focused on rather than it being decided for them for all the reasons mentioned in this body of work.)
- In my overall life right now I need more _______________. Today, I bring more of this into my mat practice by ___________________________________.

  This part can be and sound like anything. However, one completely subjective example might be, "I need more introspection." And, "I bring this in more by pausing more often to reflect how each posture is landing with me."
- My life as of late has been _____________. (for example heavy, hectic, heady, joyous, overwhelming, etc.) Postures or movements that might help counter this to bring more balance to me are _______________________.

When Facilitating:

Use affirmative language with practitioners to communicate that you believe in their abilities to figure out what they need and how to self-soothe. In page 87 of the book *Multipliers*, Liz Wiseman says that people's potential is diminished when living in fear and stress with little enjoyment. Although experienced yogis discover little fear or stress when encountering and practicing the postures, for someone with highly traumatic life experiences showing up to the mat in and of itself can be stressful. Wiseman mentions the negatively diminishing impact that dominating any environment, or room in this case, can have on the people in it. Although yoga is a special and specific practice, unique in and of itself, it is still when practiced often a facet of everyday life and therefore not excluded from the considerations appointed to any other working or social space.

The work of yoga is vigorous. Therefore, we all have an idea of how the approaches "should" be. TCY® can be practiced in conjunction with all types of yoga, whether it be hatha, vinyasa, anusara, yin, restorative, or otherwise. Furthermore, Wiseman states that, "When leaders play the role of the 'tyrant' they suppress people's thinking and capability." (p.88) The last dynamic we want to think of when we think of yoga is a tyrant. However, no matter how much we "coo", or use a lulling voice, hum, or any of the other trademarks that create a soothing and non-threatening yoga space, such as dim lighting and the like, we as yoga teachers hold an incredibly powerful position. If we try to dress that fact up any which way other than it is then it can bring incredibly deleterious effects.

This is why the TCY® method works to instill each class with heightened awareness of affirmative language, and the M.A.T. approach. In addition, the practitioner decides what their yogic path will be on the mat that day to whatever extent they like including following inner needs, completing a posture when felt is necessary, versus waiting for the teacher to designate its conclusion, hands-on researched brain areas, affirmations practiced quietly in one's head or written down, self-soothing in any relevant style, using thoughts as anchors for further discovery, creating more comfort by not always working at 'the practitioner's edge', and following one's own inner calling as to what posture or body movement is most needed at any one given point in time.

A final quote from Wiseman in *Multipliers*, and please remember this is not a book about yoga per say but a book about life and might it even be said to be a book about bringing the life out in people: "Diminishers want to verify that you understand *what they know.* They ask questions to make a point rather than to access greater insight or to generate collective learning." (p. 122) Alas, "Diminishers leave people stressed, but unstretched." Again, it might not be a book specifically about yoga as we know it in the physical format most enjoyed by many westerners but it is strikingly relevant. Facilitators on the other hand reach inside of themselves to bring out the best in people, be a cause for greater insight, and collective learning in the group as a whole.

Whether toxins enter our bloodstream, or heart-strings, it is up to us as yoga practitioners to consciously seek to remove them in order to harness well-being in our total self sense. This is one dynamic of self-agency, we strive to not only create anew but to look with new eyes into oneself. Or, as Marcel Proust said, "The real voyage of discovery consists not in seeing new sights, but in looking with new eyes." It might seem like some of the requests in the body or work of TCY® are laborious, overly-considerate, awkward, backwards, or even nonsensically tedious. Still, the fact of the matter is that trauma is a reorientation to life and pulls upon the survivor in ways that one might not imagine.

In *Trauma and Recovery,* Judith Hermann quotes Mardi Horowitz as defining traumatic life events as destroying the survivor's "fundamental assumptions about the safety of the world, the positive value of self, and the meaningful order of creation." On page 41 Herman states, "The trauma is resolved only when the survivor develops a new mental schema for understanding what happened." It can also arguably be said that this new self-identification can and must be built upon a new body narrative -- one that places the survivor in control in some of the most fundamental of ways, if not in life as a total knowing, then at least on the mat as a starting place.

The danger in yoga and for yogis is that it can be used as *or for* a kind of escapism from one's most pressing matters in life either consciously or unconsciously. The trouble of that for someone with some real material that needs to be worked through is that a divisiveness of self is consequently formed. This means that when one might start to feel heavier or more challenging feelings off the mat that are not blissful or joyful there can be a rejection of the self in that off-the-mat moment. And, therefore, a disintegration of connection to self thereby negating or dissolving all the great integration work that was done on the mat. The practice of yoga is to merge heavy and light, what is inwardly yin and outwardly penetrating.

Yoga is brilliant at merging and uniting parts of self. Therefore, yoga needs to assimilate both mentally and bodily-founded material that is present everyday for the survivor. Our job as facilitators is uniquely outlined by a statement made by Herman in her book, *Trauma and Recovery,* "restore power, reduce isolation, diminish helplessness, increase range of choice, and counter the dynamics of dominance." In our lives, perhaps both on and off the mat, an undiscovered truth is fatal. In society, we're oftentimes too scared to ask for what we need. We therefore are slow to discover other people's needs because we don't want to have uncomfortable conversations. TCY® makes it possible that no words need be exchanged other than the inner dialogue that occurs for the practitioner, as the practitioner witnesses self, and encourages self, along the way.

Chapter 6: The Pillars of Language-Building

Actively Self-Soothing

As shared, language is a huge component that is integrated into the foundation of Trauma Cooperative Yoga® classes. As a refresher, as seen at the start of the book, the foundation is in total: **M.A.T. Meeting Needs, Actively Self-Soothing, Taking Initiative.** As in traditional yoga we are schooled to observe and not react nor even actively respond to levels of discomfort in the posture unless enduring physical pain. Or, if response is necessary then do it by "breathing into it" or with focal point concentration alone. These surely are the cornerstones of the warrior mindset yet with trauma survivors we are encouraged to stay connected to self at all times, in all ways possible, so as to win against antagonistic inner states of being. These might include but are not limited to dissociating from the self; feelings of helplessness; feelings of loss of control over the self due to being encouraged not to respond to what might likely feel to the beginner of yoga as adverse physically-felt and inner-based feelings, as well as numbness or loss of connection to self, and lessened self-efficacy.

In traditional classes we might often hear, "Not to change anything" or "just observe--no need to do anything about it." The problem with that is that most trauma survivors have learned to live five inches or degrees away from the body to begin with. So, as described, encouraging reconnection at every turn possible is vital for reuniting the survivor with the ability to affect change. Whereas it might be well-meaning to assume your practitioner is best to open their eyes in warrior one posture, the reality is that this practitioner is best to gently be made aware of their choice yet realize that if they are indeed conscious of that choice made, and it serves a purpose, then it is for their best.

This actually occurred once in the author's life when in an earlier training. The teacher called out to the class that she needed to open her eyes in warrior one. In reality, the choice had been made to have the eyes closed because the author was having a difficult time connecting to her inner viscera, or inner feeling. At the time being, she was overwhelmed by feeling everyone else in the room and was more aware of everyone else but herself and her own experience. In that moment, she was working diligently with massive self-awareness to reconnect to the body felt-sense of being in the posture rather than the posture 'being her', so to speak. In the moment of being instructed from the total opposite side of the room to open her eyes she became again aware of everyone else in the room more than the inner work she was doing in the posture to therefore fully embody the posture.

Whereas we think we know best for our practitioners, the larger reality is that it is our task to make them aware of choice while not assuming we know best, or blindly taking it away from them out of a perceived notion of perfection or tradition in our own minds. Remember we are not paid to teach them everything we paid to learn from our teachers but our value is measured by the total sum of wisdom we gathered, that we found between the words and assumed interpretation of the teachings, that pertain to the people before us as they are *not as we wish for them to be.* This is difficult work to put our own egos aside and realize our work is not to impress others with how much we know but allow people to be awakened to how much they know *within* in order to wake the teacher within the practitioners, too.

Revisiting 'Actively Self-Soothing' options:

Every single posture offers up a chance to self-soothe. Let's list a few ways to implement and then you might want to take a moment to choose a few of your own favorite postures to journal about and practice how you might offer it up for the practitioners in your room to try on for size in their own practice.

Resting Pose - Traditionally Known as "Child's Pose"

You might say, "While you're resting here in whatever variation you've chosen, legs together or apart, palms forward or by your side, you might notice where there is ease in the body and where there might be tension in the body." Notice, we are mentioning the context of *ease* first in relation to the body and then mentioning the *possibility* of tension. This starts self-soothing first in the mind, and immediately empowers the practitioner.

Next, "Remember you can deepen the pose *and your connection to the pose* if you decide to introduce a self-soothing practice to this pose." This might look like, "You might choose to use the heel of your hand to draw circles on your sacrum, you might use the back of your closed hand to move up and down to iron out any tensions. The sky's not the limit, it's just a reference point here." If you are concerned about people taking the exercise too far in a way that is uncomfortable for you or another you might say, "Work along and atop your clothes line to show yourself love and compassion." It's a nice way to say there are limits as to how one might interpret self-soothing.

Two Knee Twist

From this posture we have a variety of experiences depending on the person. It's one of those postures that becomes incredibly easier for the regular practitioner yet for the person who has recently had any kind of traumatic experience it is one that requires a great level of attention and carefulness. To gain optimal support in this posture one must be greatly encouraged to focus inward on how this feels *inwardly*. This seems obvious and something that any teacher might have the practitioner before them focus on. Yet in reality because many are often focused on doing it right or perfect it is best to realize that many are considering the external alignment and skin level feeling. In order to positively combat this limiting interpretation of yoga we are conceding as facilitators to be at one with our own inner experience. Whereas we do not provide extensive backstory for why we make our bodily choices, **we can**

offer up anywhere from a one word to one sentence cause or sense that we have that requires any one particular action.

Let's explore a potential one worded self-reference:

"For those of us who are on our backs at present please consider the floor as a support for you. You might even feel as if it is meeting you and everything you need in this moment right now. Being supported. Being held. When and if it makes sense for you to do so, bring your knees into your chest with the strength of your abdomen as you continue to breathe *naturally.* From there you might pause or you might continue to bring your legs over to one side slowly with the building strength in your torso and arms that are out by your sides. As your legs are now resting on the floor, notice how it best serves you to have your knees: explore how close or far away from the arm the knees need to be in order to get the most from this stretch. Staying here with your natural breath for as long as it serves you. Once you've met your needs for your physical placement, let's consider activating our self-soothing abilities.

What does this look like for you here? For me, my rotator cuff where my arm connects into the shoulder needs some attention. So, I am going to gently press my thumb and fingers into that area. I might even do thumb circles here in the tender areas."

There are many ways we might self soothe on the mat as practitioners and suggest self soothing to practitioners. Here is some more dialogue that you might consider in this supine posture:

"In two knee twice, I often tend to fix my head in one position and miss out on a potential neck stretch. So, if it serves you then you might join me in finger presses or finger circles at the back of the head by rolling the head from side to side on the floor there right where you are. Sometimes we get more of a stretch resting our head in one direction. So, give yourself the freedom to explore here."

Or... "I notice my top leg can be even more supple. So, in order to invite the leg to open up more I am taking my closed hand nearest the top leg and gently tapping up and down it while I am maintaining my *natural* breath."

In truth, the sky is not the limit, it really is just a reference point. Really, ask anyone at NASA. Therefore, keep expanding your own interpretation and invitations to self and beyond of how you might self-soothe...

Taking Initiative

We have now gone into great detail of what self-soothing has the potential to look like and most importantly feel like. How then might we take initiative beyond the meeting of our needs and self-soothing for the TCY® formula? This portion of this book is meant to show just that and yield some insight. Why is taking initiative so important? Or, more so key and integral to this practice? The answer is simply that once again most people who suffer from post traumatic stress on a scientific level have been known to have frozen at some point during a traumatic event. The event somehow consequently got locked and stored into the body. For those who fought or fleed, the negative impression of the event is far from being minimized because in the aftermath it is often difficult for the survivor to make peace with what they had to do in order to mobilize and get away from the threat.

Moving forward it is a sad state of affairs that the survivor therefore has a difficult time trusting the self to move in a way that feels best for them. The truth is that by taking initiative as a third step versus a first or second step, the survivor of trauma, or any person at that, is far more likely to be making a cooperative, centered, and grounded decision both on and off the mat. The measures the survivor takes once having consciously *and methodically through careful deliberation* considered their needs and exercised compassion toward the self are far different in nature than the ones taken in a time of upheaval or tragedy. It is key to slowly rebuild the trauma survivor's confidence in their personal choices no matter how great or small. The yoga classroom environment is prime territory to build trust within the self again.

Therefore, how does taking initiative show up in the yoga classroom? Showing up for the self takes clarity and focus and as we've already described the preliminary hurdles and obstacles that might be present in the endeavoring of doing so. So, let's carry on. Shall we? As teachers, guides, and facilitators we are constantly inviting and encouraging our practitioners to connect and go deeper. Taking initiative is a form of great commitment to the self to go deeper. It is essential that the essential nature of initiative taking is highlighted as we are speaking to our practitioners. There are many ways to do so and in many varying tones and choice of words. Only **you** know yourself and practitioners best and are aware of what they might be most comfortable with in terms of such approaches and what motivates them the most. If you are a brand new teacher please think about listening deeply not only with your ears but from your physical heart center as you quiet your mind to hear what they are really saying with their bodies and their body movements. In between the words there exists the pulse of intuition. Listen to what is being said, and not said.

We will know when the practitioners in the room with us are **taking initiative** by observing how much free will action they take. Once you've established what options are there do they venture outside of those bounds to discover what else might be there in the posture for them? Do they look to you for every detail? Or, are they paying attention inward? As a Trauma Cooperative Yoga® facilitator, your gauge of success is not that they do everything you mention right down to the very detail like A+ academia practitioners or new recruits on a military base. The beauty of Trauma Cooperative Yoga® is that it is unlike any other land or place most people have ever been to because it is **the encouragement of safe free-will movement.** The worker bees of the world, the employees, the children in grade school, the academia practitioner as mentioned, and even those family member units in the household are perceived as successes or even lovable because they have learned to follow instructions. Let not our yoga studios be a place where success is only judged by how the external physical embodiment of an exercise is our marker of a job well done. At least, not in this form of Trauma Cooperative Yoga®.

How might you encourage people to take initiative on the mat?

This is accomplished by walking the talk. The more you freely move about within the confines of your mat at the front of the room the more they will do so themselves. In addition, the more you speak your truth behind the processes of your own practice, the more people begin to evaluate their own processes. This suggestion is not to undermine the very real and possible predicament of speaking about one's own process *too much* as a facilitator. However, so long as the sharing is done with the outlined intent to demonstrate the activation of free will on the mat, and in the succinct manner of the share ranging from one word to one sentence, then the facilitator is well-equipped to lead an effective yoga class. The primary idea, or pillar, of TCY® is to build a practice that fosters a sense of self-recuperation in the midst of the helplessness most trauma survivors feel. Leading by example is a sure fire way to stoke the fires of self-initiating behaviors. Yet, how to do so without fearing alienation by doing what no one wants to do? Speaking of oneself is often scary and seemingly self-indulgent. However, with the use of the globally unifying word, "we", from time to time in our language, there begins to be an educational component to the simultaneous action of following one's inner needs.

There is a time and place for both mediums of sharing. There is the sharing on a personal level, or on a purely instructional and functional level. If a facilitator sees the need based on class participation to share a present moment action that the body is seeking or requiring within the practice one level of sharing is to refer to the self, and the facilitator's personal practice. Another, is to use the all-inclusive "we". Whereas, talking about how a posture directly affects the self as a facilitator in one instance might be too much information or seemingly self-indulgent in another instance it kindles a trust and relatability for the class practitioners. The attendees in the classroom might be at a complete loss of what the dialogue of listening to one's body might sound like. From another vantage point, they might even distrust their own bodies which is akin to many trauma survivors' long term experience. If the author of this book cried when she experienced a low belly, parasympathetic-inducing, breath for the first time since before her pre-teen years, then it is likely that for many trauma survivors worldwide the mere act of listening to oneself is a giant leap in an unknown direction. Knowing that you're far from alone in this practice carries the practitioner a long way in their ongoing self-discovery.

Then, as for initiative taking, there is the suggested *taking action* on what is noticed and heard from within the self. In the situation that a survivor is not moving at all on their mat it is recommended that the assigned pen and paper given to each practitioner before class as a preliminary step be referred to during class time. The pen and paper are reliable anchors to becoming capable of actively and physically responding to what one is observing within their own body. As a facilitator of your own practice and of other people's yoga practices, you want to first suggest practitioners take the action of writing what is being noticed within the body. This alternative to observing through words and self-reflection is also mentioned at the start of each class. This way, the possible appearance of shame or guilt of not participating in the class at the level that practitioners might expect of themselves is thoughtfully eradicated because self-reflection was encouraged from the beginning *before* anyone might reward or penalize themselves for how their practice went.

To engage with one's body as if one might with a dear friend is a massive feat. With each step of the way there is a rumbling of positive change by merely learning how to listen to oneself. This is where modifying one's interpretation of what success may look like on the mat makes a significant long term difference of whether or not they will ever return to a yoga class at all.

How to Safeguard Against Injurious Language in the Yoga Classroom

People come to yoga for many reasons. Among these are to heal, to practice wholeness, to enjoy their bodies, to allow new feelings to arise, to cultivate existing feelings of self, to step into new sensations and an overall new sense of self. One might argue that this new version of self that one wants to cultivate more of is strong and capable. But, no one comes to Yoga to be negatively challenged or spoken to as if they simply cannot do what is being asked of them that day. That's why it is our duty as yoga teachers and facilitators to rise to the challenge of seeing people in ways they perhaps do not already see themselves.

For now, let's look at prime examples of what doesn't work and what does, *and why.*

What Doesn't Work: The second someone walks into your class they are entering the possibility of discovering themselves anew. So, consider this: do you want to walk into a room where the leader is speaking to your weaknesses, or your strengths? If you're geared toward practicing expansion and growth more often than not then you are going to adhere to the second group of those seeking facilitators or teachers who encourage your best interpretation of self forward. It is therefore our job as yoga classroom leaders to feed this positive self-identity in all aspects. When it comes to physical or sexual abuse it is oftentimes easy to target what that looks like because the offenses are often so gross in measure that it is frankly obvious what challenges the survivor faces, and therefore how the survivor needs to be spoken to in order to foster growth. However, when it comes to language the line is blurry because depending on what the person's intent is when the words are spoken the meaning changes. Unfortunately, the outcome of our words *no matter how great or loving the intention* can affect people in negative ways. That is no one's fault. That is the limitation of language.

This said, there are guidelines that lay down the potential for people to grow. Although in a perfect world this needn't be said, let's say it here and now, anyway: **If you are saying something with the intent to harm another then you are practicing violence.** There exists all kinds of boundaries in order to create healthy connections both personally and professionally. This includes mental boundaries involving language and the words chosen to speak to another. Refer to *Conquer Trauma Drama: Get Your Life Back,* also by Jo Standing, to learn more about this. We've all said things that we regret afterward or punish ourselves for in one way or another long after they've been spoken. As the old saying goes, "The tongue is the hardest muscle to control in the body." The idea is not to put so much pressure on yourself as a facilitator that you no longer are able to be real in front of a classroom when engaging the practice and practitioners. People appreciate honesty and forthrightness. However, as Siddhartha said, "All reality is but a temporary hypothesis."

Therefore, practice kindness...

We all slip sometimes but check-in, find forgiveness for yourself, and muster up an apology in the event that you may have played a damaging role in another's life, especially if it is a practitioner's life on the mat. Here are some examples of possibly injurious language in a Trauma Cooperative Yoga® class.

• *"If you're not ready."* **Why:** because this focuses on what they are NOT versus all they are in and successfully have become up until the present moment. The challenge of being completely embodied in all knowledge right out the gate of training as a yoga facilitator is a real struggle. With this in mind, if you are confirming self-negatives in class then you are welcoming the practitioner's mind to operate in a world of what they are **not** versus what they **are** capable of being in that moment. Here are some more examples of NOT language. • *"If you're not strong enough."* • *"If you're not flexible enough."* • *"If you can't balance."* (Can't is the cousin of "not".) • *"If you can't feel anything."* These phrases simply disprove your personal leadership skills. People need to reach for what they CAN DO, especially in yoga! • Another big language buster in yoga is using language that assumes negatively: for example - • *"You might not be ready for this."* • *"You might not be able to do this."*

Again, the last thing we want to do is tell people what they are capable of or might be capable of in negative terminology. On the other side of the coin saying things such as: • If you're strong enough." • "If you're flexible enough." • "If you can balance." puts people in the possible position to adversely affirm to themselves that, "I can't balance." "I am not strong enough" "I am not flexible enough" if or when they must reason a response to your verbal message as to what they're capable of in that moment, and why. The reality is we all have boundaries around our present-day abilities. Staying in a "PMA", positive mental attitude, as Napoleon Hill says, is crucial in guiding people through hardship or hopelessness.

We want to reinforce not only where people are at the present moment but honor wherever that is by using language that observes their present-day strength, flexibility, and all other internal positive seeds of ability. As facilitators we've got to believe in the best of people! They're not just coming to you as a Trauma Cooperative Yoga® facilitator to build their bodies; they're coming to you to find the strength to rebuild their lives, to form their minds into a new healthy shape, and retune their emotions so that they may begin to create new, healthy, experiences unlike the intensely traumatic ones they've come from.

Here are positive reframing options for the above language mishaps:

● Find what it means to be flexible in this moment FOR YOU... ● There are a few ways to balance in this posture we're practicing together. Here are a few options... ● Where are you right now within this posture? Are you finding a balance between your Edge of Exploration and your Known Comfort Zone? ● If you're choosing to practice this right now you may want to consider that flexibility is a strength and it takes time to build it. You're doing great by taking your time.

- Remember that where you are right now is an essential part of your journey.
- Honor where you are by practicing deep listening.
- Depending on what you're feeling here, and you may or may not be feeling anything in particular, you might practice the next variation with me.

Chapter 7: Constructing Language: A Tool for Creating Healthy Sense of Self in Trauma Cooperative Yoga®

Words have many incarnations that change shape and meaning over time, and they even acquire different interpretations from what they were originally. For example, the word 'love' is firstly a noun and then a verb. A primary example of 'love' being a verb is as given by Merriam Webster, *love is to thrive*, for example, "The rose *loves* sunlight." The word yoga is a noun, and also a verb in modern times. People in the twenty-first century say things to one another like, "Sorry, can't hang out, we're yoga-ing right now!" However, with so much yang energy focused around the doing of yoga, might it also be relevant to soften not only our gaze but our own interpretation of what it means to practice yoga? With more people than not affected by one form of traumatic life experience or another in the here and now it makes the stretching of our minds almost, if not definitely, necessary.

In the yoga-applied sense, the word 'cooperative' is used as an adjective. The word in direct opposition to cooperative is *individual.* Whereas the spiritual path is often a solo journey in the context of its purpose for self-realization, or self-liberation, the cooperative classroom is far from it. In fact, the more the teacher approaches the room as if their projections of yoga, strictly founded on their factual and book knowledge and based on prior teachings, are the aim or focus, the more of a dissonance is therefore created between the paying practitioners of yoga and the teachers themselves. It is at this time that the restrictions of hierarchy come into play. The teacher is in effect saying, "I know what you don't know and you must go through me in order to gain the knowledge you seek. This framework of teaching is the very antithesis of yoga: yoga is union.

Therefore, how might we encourage and drive people toward their inner-knowing if we as teachers insist that we are the gatekeepers to such knowing of self?

Moving forward, it is simply not enough to be sensitive toward other people in the context of a facilitator. Whereas being sensitive is undeniably essential to being cooperative, in a more modern use being sensitive is merely to sense feeling. In the past, however, being sensitive also meant "*capable* of feeling," "capable of sensing," and last but not least according to etymonline.com, *"being sensitive pertains to the faculty of the soul that receives and analyzes sensory information."* We are facilitators of yoga. In this sense, we are responsible as facilitators to "yolk" within ourselves. The onus is on us to "unite" that which is within us as we guide other practitioners of the ancient discipline of yoga. **This includes the merging of our ability to sense, with our ability to think.** Although being sensitive is a way of thinking beyond the limitations of the mind, we are far from trying to rid ourselves of our minds. We are seeking to integrate our often abandoned parts of selves with our minds, so that our minds may take a backseat, for us to be guided by a total sense of self.

Next in line, in our exploration of trauma-specific yoga, we have the expression of being trauma-informed, and teaching trauma-informed. The word 'informed' is both a noun and verb. It says you are a "thing" and that you can therefore "do". The problem with that is that we are not here on this earth to be "a thing." Nor, instruct or lead in such a way that reduces us to being "a thing" that is predictable and all alike. Therefore, we must cast aside the notion that if we teach anatomy specifically enough, or even conform to past findings by previous incarnated widely-published and followed teachers, that we are imparting what is needed by and for yoga practitioners. Specifically, if we adhere to the namely masculine way of teaching, such as in the past, we are doing a disservice to those practitioners in our rooms as facilitators.

According to an article published by *The Ministry of External Affairs* government of India, "The aim of Yoga is Self-realization, to overcome all kinds of sufferings leading to 'the state of liberation'

(Moksha) or 'freedom' (Kaivalya)." This definition exceeds any possible religious application and in that transcendence of limitations or boundaries made by another is meant to translate to the self as well. In other words, *the self's liberation and freedom* is every bit as relevant in the physical yoga practice as is any other form of yoga practice, whether that be meditation, or self-study, the study of ancient texts, or one's devotion to the branches of yogic, however that might look for the yoga practitioner, on and off the mat.

Further Along the Path

Basavaraddi goes on to say that, "Hatha (physical) yoga is a preparatory process so that the body can sustain higher levels of energy. The process begins with the body, then the breath, the mind, and the inner self." This makes great sense. The more energy we have, the more we are able to have the wherewithal to meet our day in the greatest expression of our personal abilities. This said we must admit that what builds energy, sustenance, and connection for one will not be expressed among all practitioners. It is for this reason that people go forward to create practices such as Anusara, Yin, Restorative, Power Vinyasa, and the list goes on.

However, if one is completely caught up in form even when it is an impressive lineage of yoga recently or long ago created, this over-attention to the physical embodiment of posture still limits the expressor or practitioner to be in the flow of their own energy. For, energy is not limited to the physical body in its expression and the body therefore is far from meant to fit into any mold created from an external source for too long. Or else, it becomes a sensation versus an inner bridge to greater self-knowing that eventually, as one steadily commits to practice, brings peace, freedom, and liberation.

It is therefore in Trauma Cooperative Yoga® that the idea of connecting mind, body, and spirit is no longer silent. We no longer see emotions themselves as passing clouds that are a disservice to our overall practice. Instead, we join forces in the most energetic sense to consensually commit to not only be present but to activate the longing for the otherwise latent self to be within the felt senses and answer their calling. This might look like finding language that works *into* the newly-designed intention alongside our forefront ambitions to be great teachers and facilitators.

Language that is plainly spoken is the best type of language for the reason being that when someone is working through a traumatic event although the event is now past the frontal lobe, or executive thinking of the brain, can be challenged in an unhelpful way. Therefore, omitting the use of too many long and lengthy spiritual words, or Sanskrit words, as beautiful sounding and resonating to the soul as they are, can be *extremely helpful* in aiding focus for the trauma specific practitioner. If one is therefore able to focus on simple words then a sense of self-containment, and self-security, arises from within. As a large statement, it's the simple things that impact us the most in life. Whereas the yoga mat is a great opportunity to be a vehicle for the survivor to become free of immobilization, as brought on by being in a rush of confusion, caused by the wake of having been in a tragedy beforehand, or type of violence, confusion itself can be brought on by the difficulty of fathoming a potentially overly-leading intellect of a good-natured facilitator. Remember, as a facilitator to bring in your other moral attributes, too.

The Sensing Self

Now, let's focus on *constructively engaging* the thinking self, or frontal lobe, while simultaneously learning to tune into our brain stem area, also known as our 'sensing self,' or primal self. The sensing self can get a bad rap when or if people point to it as having limited function, or relevance to daily life. In TCY® we learn to engage the sensing self as it is more than a messenger of "eat or kill" or "run, or hide." The sensing self is to the feeling self as the logical brain is to the abstract thinking hemisphere of the brain. They feed one another in communication of what is taking place in our physical external environment, and are key parts in one another's functioning. The logical part of self can rationalize oneself into creating a new direction in life based on initially stimulating abstract information. For example, if one senses something appealing about a place when one is vacationing, and the feeling of connectedness to that geographic location is very strong, the logical self can then convince the self through in-depth cogitation that this place on the map is meant to become home in the near future. The abstract non-physicalized self, although in relationship to the logical brain in this formative role, often is a precursor to the personal choices one makes in life whether conscious, or unconscious.

The cause for the above explanation is the need to realize that the sensing self may want to tell us a new story other than the boiled down feelings and decisions stemming from the black and white perception of love and fear. For as we develop the "in between" sensing that comes between the inclination to strictly fear or love we become more able to explore the self that oftentimes gets locked into these definites or opposites. Yet, when given a strict course of action where choice is limited, although it might be present to some degree, we tend to cease exploration whether it be inner or otherwise. Whereas repeated actions are healthy in forming a level of discipline and a sense of perceived safety in knowing what to expect next there are no absolutes in any course of study. This includes self-study, or otherwise. For instance, when one perceives what is to come next before the moment has come because they have practiced the series of movements countless times the body is actually more prone to injury because consequently less actual thought oftentimes referred to as mindfulness goes into movement.

Just as with the body so is as with the mind. If we anticipate definite parameters of who we are and what we like then we limit the range of discovery that is possible. Additionally, we might assume we 'like' or 'need' something when really if we were to be listening in the moment we realize that what it is that we require is very different from what it is we have been programmed to desire based solely on what we have been programmed to practice. It is for this reason that in TCY® we stretch beyond the body's prior stories no matter how precious they are or how loved the teacher is, or the studio, or geographic location is, where the initial idea came from.

In TCY® we encourage ourselves to listen more deeply and move more freely. Nothing in the self needs to change in order to do so. We only need to become more willing to dissolve the stiffness of ideas passed down for generations both on and off the mat. For instance, one yoga practitioner stringently followed the foot positions for warrior one for many years. However, as a female she has wider hips than the original male-only inhabitants of yoga practice. Therefore, although one woman was welcomed to learn to practice in 1937, known as Indra Devi, the details of the very practice continued to be for the male body. This said, rather than the front heel lining up with the back heel in warrior one, the feet likely need to be wider, in consideration of the width of the practitioners' hips.

This mention suits the anatomical fact that women's hips are *wider* than mens. And, since the hips are in direct relationship to the knees and ankles then this might make sense for you.

Sense.

In order to sense, from the body, rather than from ideas passed down, we gain greater self-mastery *because our answer is coming from our own exploration.* Said yoga practitioner ended up causing indefinite pain to her knees from the pull and strain when then following the next cue to bring the back hip forward in order to "square" the hips to the front of the room. Although this *looks* amazing to both the trained and untrained eye we must remember that all training came from somewhere and sometimes that training is founded on dated beliefs.

There is nothing more beautiful than a yogi honoring the lineage from which one's practice comes from just as there is nothing more sincere about the lover of life than the child who reveres the parent. However, not all parents nor teachers act in a holy manner nor do they all practice holiness. To be holy is to honor the inner-intelligence of all beings. This is not just a statement but an invitation to be courageous enough to step into the unknown within the self in order for other practicing practitioners to do the same. We must reach deeper from within ourselves in order to rise higher. Our roots will exist for all of time and on a wide scale those very roots need to be examined closely. Just as with a person who wants to heal, a lineage that continues to want to become realized must challenge the very legs from which it stands.

Integration of Self

Once we independently and collectively acknowledge where we come from we then begin the great process of integration. On the yoga mat in TCY® we are welcomed to spend the last ten minutes after final resting posture to either journal one's stream of consciousness thoughts or to practice the stream of one's own thoughts in the presence of another seeker, or yogi, on the mat. Both present options as to how one might approach the mental self-integration into the great, and ever-reaching, practice of yoga is more than fine. In the below one exercise is presented for consideration of the active facilitator.

THE FACILITATION OF "YES. AND?"

The phrase, "Yes. And?",when done in the following capacity lends a chance to integrate past, present, and projected future more fully so that one may live as cohesively and productively as possible.

STEP 1: find a partner.

STEP 2: designate who is the speaker for this first round and who is the responder. After this round the speaker and responder will switch roles.

STEP 3: Have the speaker choose from one of the following starter sentences that are affirmative in nature or come up with their own "I AM" statement.

Example Starter Sentences:

→ I am so lucky.
→ I am learning what it means to be fully healthy.
→ I am curious about many things.
→ I am proud of who I am.
→ I am seeking more _____ in life.
→ I am becoming more confident.

And, the list of possibilities for starter sentences beginning with **"I AM"** go on.

STEP 4: Have the speaker say their chosen "I AM" statement out loud while looking directly at the responder. Simply state these words, nothing more, nothing less, in whatever way feels natural for you at present.

STEP 5: When the speaker pauses after stating the "I AM" statement now the responder says the two simple words, **"Yes. And?"** Nothing more, nothing less, is said.

STEP 6: The speaker says whatever comes to mind. Try to speak for no longer than 30 seconds at a time before pausing again. Each round lasts only 5 minutes in total. The speaker should not speak unstoppingly for longer than one minute max before the responder says, **"Yes. And?".** There is collective power in pausing where one is often literally able to collect themself and stop the self from repeating overused thought patterns or thought leanings. If the responder needs to keep time within a quiet timer or stopwatch to keep everyone on track then please do so.

STEP 7: Once the speaker has paused for five consecutive seconds the responder says, "Yes. And?" It is key for the responder to speak as naturally as possible. As well as, to be neutral and non-negatively judging in tone. The speaker must lend themself to the unknown as a neutral listener as it is never certain that someone means what one thinks is being said.

STEP 8: Continue back and forth like so until five whole minutes have effectively passed.

STEP 9: When the timer sounds please make sure to bow to your partner and include the verbal salutation of namaste.

STEP 10: Change active roles now by having the speaker become the responder and the responder role is to be inhabited by the former speaker.

Re-Collection of Self

It's key to remember that the disruption of regular thought patterns or ways of thinking, such as is often the case after trauma, can feel unsafe or even scary. If you are practicing this and have little to no resistance to the courage it takes to try something new and possibly with someone you've never met then please practice great restraint. This means to calmly pause when the exercise is complete and refrain from commenting on how "good" or "amazing" or "interesting" the exercise was for you, or on how they did, unless asked by your partner. Remember that we all have scar tissue and not all is visible. Some remain in the brain or heart or elsewhere within the visceral self.

Give room for the mental practice and mental component of practice to gel, or, "yolk," for both yourself and the other practitioner you are working with for this round. If personal change were so easy, or produced overnight, then everyone would be at their apex all the time. This is not the case nor even 'should' it be. Some of the best 'things' in life are hard won. Please be patient with yourself as well as with your partner for the exercise. Just as one would not in this day and age hopefully *push* a practicing yoga practitioner into a posture we all are best served being kind and gentle with one another. We must assume that no one is doing this work for us and therefore we have little to do with the inner equation of what makes them whole, happy, or comfortable in this process.

Be okay with the process. Ground and breathe just as you do in a yoga posture, whether that be the **Meeting of your needs in the posture, Actively self-soothing in the posture, or the Taking of Initiative** to find a new way that works best for you. As mentioned in prior writing the **M.A.T.** learning curve is one that builds a greater sense of safety, self, and emphasizes positive personal power.

Relaying Reality

Language is very important when asking one to engage with and move their body. If as a facilitator it is said, "Now, I am going to move my left foot up in the air." it's not as effective as trying the following words, "I am slowly drawing in my low belly to protect my low back as I lift my foot off the floor", this is far more conducive for building trust and connection. In creative writing training the rule of thumb is, "Show, don't tell". This keeps people's attention. This creates intrigue as to what the character in focus will do next.

However, in yoga, as an art form of living from a state of union, both the actions *and* the words are supposed to match. The need for suspense itself is an egoic structure that says the world is unworthy of our attention unless we are entertained, or intrigued, in some way. The yoga practice room is meant to be an honest journey from the inside out. Not an example of how creative or mighty the facilitator is.

If language alone is not enough in the TCY® practice room, although direction-yielding as it is, then what helps our chosen thoughts really *land* in the listening ear as being *real* and worthy of following? In one simple word: experience. Personal experience to be more exact. Experience adjusts the psyche to a new truth. Perhaps, equally if not more rewarding, hard won and carefully considered personal experience also recalibrates the body, or soma, to a new knowingness. One can rationalize, analyze, or even perfectly follow a set of mat instructions day in and day out, and *still* not completely become in touch with their own truth of what exists and needs to be heard, *and moved,* from within their own body.

We as teachers think or assume that people just want to walk into the yoga classroom and follow a set of instructions while foregoing any need to think at all. However, that is just what we as people have largely been programmed to do. It is to our demise as trauma specific yogis to continue to carry out blind following as in this case when the body calls the being is not listening. Instead, the idealistic mind is dutifully following exactly what is being asked of it in order to gain some kind of physical enlightenment and mastery that at its best is fleeting.

The physical self is never an area of self that is meant to grasp onto ideas laid out by another. Although we were lucky enough to have been born into bodies, that is the extent of our commonalities when it comes to the human body. Some bodies invert more at the joints, limbs don't appear fully straightened on either side of the joints, and some have stiff muscles prone to early onset arthritis. We can never assume any one thing about another person's body. The commonality more apparent in people is the basis of the soul's desire to belong. Unfortunately, many of us will do whatever it takes to do just that. Whether it unknowingly causes long term damage to total well-being of self, the physical body, or not.

It is our best aim as facilitators to awaken the knowing and "rightful rightness" within each yoga practitioner who shows up in our yoga room. Contraindications and safe movement procedures are what are owed to the practitioners before us. Beyond that it is the pathway to personal freedoms and liberations that we must lead. We must remember that personal experience leads the way in all things longlasting and is a precursor to any necessary long term change. Experience tells the body and mind that whatever the projection is that the newfound reality has in fact arrived.

Trust people to know what is right for them. Trust yourself to share what is necessary in order to lay down the path for the best chance at inner listening.

Reconstructing Thought

Studies show that when even mildly stressed thinking faculties are compromised. Most people in the state of Post Traumatic Stress who are entering the yoga classroom have very little time to form original thought in their day to day. They likely have become so highly-attuned to doing what is either asked of them or what is already learned by rote that the idea of original or organic thought is foreign. Thankfully, this is not life-threatening. However, it is negatively-impacting one's quality of life. A study by the *National Institutes of Health* puts it this way, "The response to stress is not just a primal reaction affecting parts of the brain that are common to a wide array of species ranging from salamanders to humans. Stress, in fact, can cripple our most advanced mental faculties."

In order to properly marry body and mind as yoga represents is a primary aim we need to spend time equally in both in the yoga classroom. If we previously thought that stress is an issue that can easily be handled by physically working out then we need to realize that whereas it is difficult to engage the advanced area of the brain, otherwise known as the frontal lobe, during stressful times, to completely disengage from conscious directed thought we are impeding the learning curve through Post Traumatic Stress that leads to Post Traumatic Growth. In effect, if we as facilitators ask the yoga facilitators who have entrusted their practice to us to "follow their gut" and "carve their own way" by giving ways to healthily and safely engage with self, we are aiding a significant recovery step.

The desire to lead with our knowledge is valid and deserves to be at the forefront of our sharing therefore by which we notably express wisdom by also including our own experience. As we do so, we ask the practitioner to modify the posture not just from a termed "beginner" to "intermediate" or "advanced" form of it but in such a way that speaks to the meeting of their needs as a whole person. This includes mentally, emotionally, physically, and perhaps yes even spiritually. If someone needs to feel "larger than life" then bringing an arms wide open variation to an otherwise "straight forward" or "pre-destined" posture such as warrior one might meet an inner craving to expand while also addressing mental or emotional resistance that sits in the practitioner's body to "take up space" in the world. This consideration involves physical, mental, spiritual, and emotional components of self for both facilitator and practitioner.

When we exercise the option to meet personal needs in the moment--and yes even on such ancient grounds as the yoga mat--we naturally flow into the second aspect of TCY® which is to *self-soothe.* As we self-soothe oxytocin is released. This increases feelings of felt personal safety and therefore effectively reduces stress hormones. At that point, the frontal lobe is online again, personal choice has returned, and the overarching goal of self-mastery can begin to be reached right there in the present moment. As spiritual as it can feel to be doing the same thing as everyone else in the yoga classroom, in exact matching bodily tempo, imagine how it might feel to connect inwardly to the innate and guiding intelligence within *and* be surrounded by emboldened and impassioned people courageously also following the beat of their own drum.

More Than a Break From the Day

Yoga's soothing and balancing abilities have larger considerations than being just a worry-free break from the day. If as facilitators we slow down enough to bring the executive facilities back online again. This small yet impactful engagement of the frontal lobe, also known as the prefrontal cortex, or simply speaking: thinking brain, can have wondrously wide reaching effects. When the frontal lobe is supported in being "online" through these simple decision-making processes, that are brought forward as often and calmly as possible, it translates to the following mental abilities that this invisible to the eye area behind the forehead is responsible for: concentration, planning, decision making, insight, judgment and the ability to retrieve memories.

Imagine how supportive returning to the M.A.T. principles throughout your yoga class can be for yoga practitioners!

It is perhaps because yoga is so beloved and praised in one's life independently and collectively that some yoga teachers believe that one's private yoga practice should never be shared for the sake of observation alone. It is the belief by some teachers from a more traditional vein of yoga that yoga itself is meant to be verbally shared and demonstrated only for teaching's sake. But, that "yoga practitioners", of which every yoga leader is always meant to be at heart, no matter if they professionally teach or not, should "never be able to view their yoga teacher's private practice." That's how the author learned it, anyways. This might make sense in some contexts. However, in the train of thought that TCY® yields to, this type of thinking only aggrandizes the teacher in an egoic sense and further creates a hierarchical relationship between practitioner and teacher. In the spirit of TCY® people go to yoga to come into contact with the spirit within, and to learn from the spirit and wisdom of the facilitator, while expanding within the reaches of their own.

If a teacher's central focus is to showcase all that they know, and the particulars of how best to do a "beginner" or "advanced" version, then it might be that other components of yoga in the long haul are lost. When the movements chosen by the facilitator as the focus of class are from a primary series then this allows the easeful pulling in of additional self-care references such as self-touch. Whereas self-touch can be an intimidating suggestion to make to anyone, nevermind to the trauma-specific population, when done without being either mechanical, nor too sensual that it seems sexual, it is safe to say that the practitioner will interpret it as an accent to the health modality of yoga, and nothing more...and surely nothing negative.

In the consideration of introducing self touch as a self-soothing addition to the practice of yoga on and off the mat, language is as much of the essence than it ever is. For example, the use of words or phrases such as, “try hand drags; gently press with the thumb; apply the heel of your hand to any area that feels it might need some support in softening,” is better than the use of words or phrases slightly more suggestive such as “*massage* your leg”, or “*slide* your hand alongside”, or “*rub* your buttock where you feel pain.” These expressions can go awry for the yoga practitioner who has been affected by trauma in a sexual way.

In the trauma-affected population, when practicing yoga, the tendency is to disconnect and cut off from the body. When the teacher says, “focus on your breath through the discomfort” it is helpful to a degree and to a point. However, what if the facilitator says, “I feel discomfort here today/sometimes; in order to stay with this posture and listen to my experience I am honoring my process by calming this area as much as I might need to. Therefore, I am gently pressing down with the heel of my own hand in the crease of my upper thigh to help ground me through this. You might also try the same. Or, something else that makes the most sense to you.”

There is a service offering more than the option to either go to the mainstays of resting/child's pose or downward facing dog. In the initial beta test group run of TCY® training people reported being able to stay with postures longer, more calmly, and in a more centered way because they chose to integrate various methods of self-soothing as introduced by the lead trainer and author of this book. Some practitioners said that they didn’t wake up sore the next day after their practice as they had in practices prior because they were spending more time integrating the work on the mat through the actual process of yoga practice. There is the saying that it’s difficult to focus on more than one thing at a time. Or, to have an over awareness of something unpleasant if there is something pleasure-inducing happening at the same time. In this way, TCY® draws upon the practitioner's ability to self-love, self-reference, and self-determine one's own experience.

The University of Queensland in Australia says that there is mounting evidence that a system in the brain called the cholinergic system acts like a master switch that then allows the brain to identify which sensory input is worthy of attention and then "shines a spotlight" on that input. This is far from to say that sensory input on the yoga mat should be downright ignored. It is however healthily being responded to and replaced with a different point of bodily focus, or bodily "drishti", as the sanskrit word is that means focal point. As previously detailed, when the brain is stressed due to traumatic triggers parts of the brain go offline. In the construction of a whole person, and in advocating for whole self healing, it is therefore paramount to keep all "self structures"that necessitate a healthy human "online", or able to be engaged. Simply put, if the practitioner is unable to reach the part of self that consciously and carefully drives its master movements aka the command center, or frontal lobe, then there is danger present for any practitioner.

Given our job as yoga facilitators is to eradicate any unnecessary threats to the practitioners' well-being on the mat it is therefore imminent to consider prioritizing the practitioner's immediate comfort in order to keep the "alarm systems" of the brain at ease and therefore the practitioner as a whole at ease. In order to stay in a state of peacefulness the amygdala, aka the alarm system, and the hypothalamus, aka the firing system of toxic chemicals into the adrenals, needs to be thoughtfully looked out for in advance. This can be done by adding in extra consideration by the facilitator. If **self-soothing** aids in keeping toxic feelings, chemicals, and states of mind at bay by releasing oxytocin then in the spirit of being whole-self inclusive we must honor this practice with this in mind.

Furthermore, the words we choose are instrumental for the defining of the experience of the practitioner on the yoga mat. In a study conducted by Pereira F., Detre G. & Botvinick M. at Princeton University in a completely phenomenal fashion scientists are now able to look at brain activity in an fMRI and based on the images predict what it is the subject is thinking about in pictures. Whereas as TCY® facilitators we far from desire to read minds we *do* wholeheartedly desire to awaken more self-knowing on the mat. The Princeton article says that the long term goal is to then be able to convert the knowledge of the pictures that are held in one's mind into the words that one is likely thinking about. The report says that the intention is to have more general knowledge of the brain, in so many words.

Let's pause in a sacred stretch of the mind for a moment: if people go to such great lengths to analyze the minds and beings of others with such unflinchingly stupendous results as that then what might happen if we as people express as much interest in our own inner processes? Throughout time the world has known many gifted teachers and spiritual leaders and even those with psychic tendencies. Yet, as yoga practitioners we know that we must first focus on ourselves in order to have a chance in the world to be what it is we dream to be. Yoga is a haven which has the potential to allow the human soul to reside in peace for the duration of a practice, and even potential wonder. For the anatomically-inclined, as was recognized in the early 1990's by the National Center of Biotechnology, there is no part of human anatomy that is more intriguing than the brain. Today we are being called as yoga facilitators to continue to dive deep into whole self supporting with all parts of self involved.

Part Two |

Becoming the Soul of the Survivor

Chapter 8: Learning the Survivor's Experience

Responding to Realness

In order to be real with people we need to respond to who they are in the moment. People's abilities, and even ways of expressing, change depending on how they are feeling that day, and what they're up against or most challenged by. In Dr. Peter Levine's book, *Trauma and Memory,* he is quoted, "To be traumatized is to be condemned to an endless nightmare, replaying these unbearable torments, as well as being prey to various obsessions and compulsions." Therefore, it is important to expect to see things in the classroom that you're not expecting or accustomed to seeing. Behaviors, sounds, gestures, and perhaps you might notice a practitioner being overly connected with, or not connected at all, to specific parts of their own body.

When the author was becoming a yoga teacher, she first trained in Pilates. This was due to the fact that in public yoga practice the enormity of both her body sensations, and emotional feelings, flooded her, and were too overwhelming for her upon initially attending studio classes. The result of attending yoga classes, not oriented in Trauma Cooperative Yoga® principles, was nothing short of temporarily devastating for her as a yoga practitioner. Her first yoga class in Richmond, Virginia resulted in her quickly leaving the room after tears welled up in her eyes. She hadn't known this kind of emotion but in very rare instances throughout her life such as her dad and high school boyfriend passing away. She didn't understand the great appearance of such strong feelings, or where they were coming from, nor did she feel that she could safely face them in a traditional classroom centered solely on a physical workout.

This same experience of having to leave the class due to an inward rising of strong feelings occurred again when she attended a vinyasa class in Nelson, British Columbia. In her next attempt to rectify the issue of extreme overwhelm, and manage the intrusion of bodily memories, she went to the back of the room in a Los Angeles class. That seemed to work well enough as the teacher left her to her practice on the mat. However, being new to the practice she really needed the care and attention to detail that was absent hidden at the back of the class. Soon thereafter, the author learned about the Pilates contrology exercises, a practice of how to gain control over what one is experiencing within their own body, as created by Joseph Pilates for World War I survivors. During her initial Pilates teacher training, she came to experience her own dissonance with her Pilates Teacher Trainer, due to a non-Trauma Cooperative Yoga® school setting.

The teacher trainer came over to Jo and directed her legs over her head without any warning or asking beforehand if she may assist her. As a new practitioner, who hadn't often experienced this degree of motion in her body other than as a preteen gymnast, Jo immediately felt startled and panicked. But, more than anything, scared. As a practitioner practitioner, she felt conflicted with whether to say anything, or not, to the leading teacher trainer. She feared mentioning the discomfort, or making a request for a heads up before her teacher possibly initiated touch in the future, that it might create conflict, and jeopardize her earning of her certification.

It is key to be aware that Jo did not want to feel the way she had. Nor, did she want, or expect, the physical body sensations that came up for her along with the unannounced physical contact. Nevertheless, the inability to say anything, or make a request, due to her fear of alienating herself from the teacher, and training, was essentially what became of the situation. The discomfort felt, and consequent fear present, created a distance, and distrustfulness, between herself, and the teacher trainer all the way through the last day.

The trainer's unconscious incompetence in creating a trauma aware environment for trainees created a distance between the two in what was otherwise a potentially empowering relationship. It is worth mentioning, that we are all capable of being insensitive, no matter how hard we try or school not to be, as trauma creates unexpected side effects depending on both the person and situation. The missing step to instill a safe place for practitioners is to provide an overview of boundaries, and possible class outcomes, from the outset. Unfortunately, the possible connection was further thwarted by the trainer negatively judging the trainee's necessary *emotional* withdrawal from class. This was her only known way to self-preserve at the ripe young age of 21 because it felt safest to withdraw the part of herself that had been affected...

In the present day, the author might use the curiosity that was also present in that moment for her to have anchored her in a sense of safety in a mental and thus physical way that might've then brought about a sense of calm. So, in this way, she might have stayed present to the other attendees, and the general class dynamics, instead of shutting down. As Peter Levine says, in his book, *Trauma and Memory*, "How might we work with rather than against them, (the memories) accessing and utilizing their "compressed energy" to liberate us from their stranglehold?" The key is to learn how to use the experience itself to direct us toward where there is light and learning instead of stewing in confinement and restriction.

Mind you, the survivor *must* be equally as curious about the learning, as they are interested in being enveloped by feelings of lightness, such as joy, and ease, in order to successfully eliminate the residue of the past from present experience. As teachers, we facilitate this by having an objective standpoint when it comes to what we most readily perceive as being strictly good, or bad, in the scope of the human experience on the mat. As far as Peter Levine's quote from his book, *Trauma and Memory* goes, we might explore what is meant by compressed energy. As with all people, irrespective of the nature of their life experiences, we hold energy. This energy is neutral. It is neither inherently good, nor bad, unless we make it so. This quote is great at illustrating that point.

In regards to nutrition, one of the author's favorite quotes is by Einstein. It goes like this, "Food is sunlight condensed into matter."

The word 'real' might even be placed before the word food in this sentence. Just like real food is grown in the sunlight, and carries sunlight in its every bite, the real nature of our feelings is dependent on whether or not we see ourselves as being at the axis of change in our lives. We cannot feel in charge, nor make change evident in our lives, if we do not see each exchange that occurs within us, whether it's sensation, feeling, emotion, or action, as a key part of who we are in that moment. Our ability to be resilient errs on the side of realizing that there is much that occurs within us, and within us much we can change.

Intentional Activation

The way of the warrior in yoga is not only to form the posture known as such but to activate within the self what is necessary in order to have command over the self in challenging times. The hedonist, or one-sided pleasure seeker, will only desire what feels good in the practice. Whereas in yoga we often are taught how to manage the physical, mental, or emotional hardships within the span of our practice it is revolutionary to conjure and care for the challenging moments so that in one's daily life movement the warrior may best carry on.

The survivor learns to carry on by closing that past window of time that is often highlighted by disconnect, disharmony, and disease. For example: we often use breath to manage the tensions but not to call them up. However, the more we may become acquainted with the inner turmoil the quicker we are able to steer and neutralize our lives to a place of free will movement again that is not determined nor blindsided by the rise of challenging moments within. By learning to call the unpleasantries forward as part of our physical movement practice we are sharpening our resolve for trauma resolution by creating fierce *inner* resolve that finally results in our attainment of long sought after peace.

Reconciling Fragmentation - Becoming Whole Again

Part of the sense of being disconnected is in the literal feeling within the self of being cut off from parts of one's own self. It is scary and terrifying for someone trying to relearn self-control and the calm that comes from it. Therefore, a yoga practice of mind and body is often helpful. The seat of a posture is inhabited, such as upright seated posture. Then, the invitation is made for the practitioner to put their hands on their head in the three primary brain areas while saying, "What is in my mind," then hands on the heart, "Is in my heart." Then, hands on the center of the abdomen, "Is in my core." Finally, hands on tops of legs, "Is in my being." We are carried forward by our legs. They allow us to be in this world in most cases although if one is in a wheelchair then one might replace the hand position for the last mind mantra to be placed on the mobilizing force of the body. Which in this case would be the arms.

Body as Story

It is key to remember as we guide people in our classes that stillness does not necessarily mean that someone is numb or scared, and active engagement of movement does not necessarily mean that a person can feel what is occurring within their body. This recognition of body circumstance is instrumental in persevering as a teacher-facilitator to maintain a state of neutralness. Being neutral in how we approach our next direction, as we observe practitioners, and their likely present and next needs within the classroom, takes place both in our minds' thoughts, and our interactive cues.

Dr. Peter Levine in his groundbreaking work recognizes the body based emergency responses at a time of needing to secure one's survival. They are bracing, contracting, retracting, fighting, fleeing, and freezing, as well as setting and maintaining territorial boundaries. Although, in your yoga class, a practitioner is unlikely to be bracing themselves, or contracting away from threat in the immediate environment, the body remembers it's perceived-to-be "saving grace" movements, that in turn supports the survivor to feel even an inkling of safety, or connection to the self. Since everyone's body is entirely different from the next, in addition to the experiences that each body has had in its lifetime, each survivor has their own realizations to innately come to terms with. It is our job as teachers and guides of yoga to propose a gentle reaching into areas that are challenging in an effort to healthily-reorient the survivor to the felt experiences both within the body, as well as how the body is apt to *experience* the world at large, *interact* with the world at present, and *orient* to the self off of the mat.

Stories in the Body

There are various forms of body memories that lead into the phenomenon we call flashbacks. As far as flashbacks themselves go there are a couple of forms of flashbacks that become apparent for the survivor. In an easy to remember format these are divided into three "V" sections for this book as designed by the author: **Visual, Visceral, and Volatile.** The last one listed as "volatile" does not necessarily comply with the norm as far as definition goes. However, the emotional self that the word it is describing is acknowledged as being highly-unpredictable, and oftentimes puzzling. Hence, the word volatile being used here.

Seeing as the world does not often welcome spontaneity, or a full range of emotional expression, emotion itself is oftentimes perceived as frightening. Therefore, the word volatile is used. Words often found to be synonymous with volatile are tense, strained, uneasy, uncomfortable, charged, explosive and turbulent. Coincidentally, these words are often used to describe how one feels *when one does not understand the emotions surging within.* On the contrary, the states of being found within these words are noticeable in a person, or survivor, when they are being afflicted by an intense range of emotion that is even unbeknownst to themselves as to where it comes from.

Let's start with **visceral flashbacks.** Visceral flashbacks are an intense bodily recollection of an event. As we look at the root of the very word "visceral" itself it is found to have been used in the 1570s, French, meaning to "affect inward feelings," and directly from Medieval Latin, *visceralis,* meaning "internal," as well as from Latin *viscera*, plural of *viscus* "internal organ, inner parts of the body." The definition itself, when boiled down to it, means relating to the viscera, or the visceral nervous system, and relating to deep inward feelings stored in the body rather than intellect. All of these basic references from dictionaries point to the remembering in the body. Or, as Dr. Bessel van der Kolk says and titles his well-regarded book, *"The Body Keeps The Score."*

What then are we capable of when our bodies remember? In what direction must we lead ourselves when our bodies remember challenging pasts? How might we as teachers best hold space for when someone has a visceral flashback?

The first obvious statement is that we do not know when someone is having a visceral flashback by merely looking at them. Our best guide as teacher-facilitators as to how best to manage visceral flashbacks is to first look within ourselves, and how we modify our awareness, as well as felt experience, in response to a visceral flashback. Then, we are made more aware of how to best facilitate a class that works with people where they're at in the moment. Both living from a place of, and facilitating, containment is a key element to surviving the misplacements of self caused by visceral flashbacks. The remembering in our bodies distances us from what is at present the reality within, before and around us. How then might we address visceral flashbacks? As well as how we might then give back to our practitioners and their well-being from this newfound place of awareness that springs from within.

Visual Flashbacks

Like visceral flashbacks, visual flashbacks are difficult to target whether another person is having one unless the practitioner tells you directly that they are experiencing one. This is only because unless we are in a highly specialized lab with the proper equipment we cannot see within someone's brain, or even our own for that matter. However, if someone has removed eye contact for a long period of time, or no longer has an obvious eye direction, combined with pained facial expressions then it might be an indicator that they are at the very least disconnected from the visual component of the practice as offered up by the facilitator.

They might have a different "picture show" running through their mind, other than the one containing the present moment, and present room, or setting. In this case, it is best to serve the practitioner by giving the class the general cue without naming names, *"As I become aware of my own, you also might bring your attention to your eye muscles for a moment. Let's soften our eye muscles."* You might also suggest, *"I'm bringing my hands together to create connection between my left and right brain hemispheres. As I find my breath again, and wherever it needs to be in my body now."* As a facilitator of your own practice, and other practitioners' practice you might bring the chance for people to take in the room around them both within their yoga mat and beyond their yoga mat for a moment, while staying on the contained space of their mat. Once that is practiced for a moment, you might encourage people to bring their eye focus back to the space of their own mat, continue to notice through sensing, and visually watching, as the breath rises and gently moves the edges of their own body to expand with each inhalation. The practitioners' re-embodiment of present day visioning can be greatly assisted by shifting the eye muscles to different focal points in order to develop a greater relationship with the practitioners' immediate surroundings.

Volatile *aka Emotional* Flashbacks

We'd like to think that each component of the self can be remedied by addressing or confronting that part of the self. However, such as with an emotional flashback the reality, and therefore the axis of power, might lay within another component of the self other than purely the emotional alone. As with the other types of flashbacks, it is difficult to know if someone is experiencing this form of psychosomatic recollection on the mat, or not. If a teacher knows a practitioner well, and therefore can discern the facial muscle differences, and body language, particular to that person, then it is definitely possible that the facilitator might be able to tell if the practitioner is experiencing a universally uncomfortable emotion. Let it be known, this type of flashback is a cornerstone of independent healing when met with intelligence and compassion.

Oftentimes, we might see puckered or stressed facial muscles as being an indicator of a challenging emotion coming up. The great news is, if we act with discernment, in regards to seeing the emotion, whichever it is, as beneficial versus adversarial, then healing is integrative in that moment for the practitioner. If we notice this type of internal happening from the outside we of course cannot be sure that they are indeed feeling what we might infer they are feeling. Therefore, it is essential to refrain from labeling the feeling, or emotion, even within one's own mind as a leader, within the facilitation process.

However, it is radically supportive to hold space impartial to what emotions one might prefer as a leading facilitator for practitioners to have in the classroom. It is key to mention here again that if you are aware of someone crying, to come to one's rescue is unnecessary. In the event that tears are streaming and not connected with any loud interrupting noises or accompanying danger-invoking body movements, then doing anything at all is guaranteed to be non-essential for that person's integral healing. It is too often that a box of Kleenex is slid across the floor to quickly remedy or quieten the occurrence of tears. *This interrupts the person's natural flow of energy* that is in the moment oriented toward discharging what might be a long held pattern in either the emotional, mental, physical, or spiritual self.

In the event of someone having a noticeably difficult time breathing, is in physical danger, or who is making loud sobbing sounds, it might best serve to invite everyone in the classroom to calmly stop what they are doing in order to share in a collective pause. The words might be, "I notice we are moving a lot of energy. Everyone deals with that in different ways. Sometimes staying with your current posture, or moving to a new one, or taking a break altogether from your practice to journal or use the bathroom is best to self-soothe." Chances are there is a lot happening in the room in response, or reaction, to the newly-introduced group dynamic of extreme feeling, and consequent emotion. The person crying up a storm is likely to feel self-conscious, and feel as if they are the only person in the room because they literally don't have the ability to hold space for anyone's emotion or feeling other than their own.

The suggested words might serve to destigmatize the intense emotion, as well as to expand the person's feeling, perhaps long held, and remind them that they have a supportive community around them to feel what they feel. You might then follow with, *"Let's find stillness in a comfortable position. Whatever that might look like for you. I am sitting here for five to ten breaths before moving on to the next practice on my mat. I invite you to deeply notice where you're at and extend a great deal of love and compassion for wherever it is you are within your practice."* Finally, offer a way out, *"If after you count your five or ten breaths, you want to lie down on your mat, and perhaps put your hands on your stomach, or your chest, feel free to do so. If you absolutely must leave, then please come back after the class ends, in order to touch base with me. If you have to completely leave the building, then please feel free to come early to class next time to talk to me. If you like."*

Auditory Flashbacks

Although not given a special section in this book, auditory flashbacks are natural just as all the rest and can be triggered through a sound that is reminiscent to the sounds present at the time of a trauma, or multiple traumas. How far back the sound connection goes in time, and how often, of course determines the depth of the impact of the said proposed auditory flashback. Just because the flashback is on a sound level does not mean that it starts as a sound flashback, or will end there for the individual. This is why it is so crucial in your class planning to forecast all sounds that might be present in the classroom, as well as outside of the classroom.

Write on a white board instead of a chalkboard. The sound difference will land with the practitioners. Is your air conditioner functioning best, or might it put off loud sounds that can be scary? Is there traffic outside close to the building? If yes, remind the people in the class that this is a possibility, or of any other loud sounds that might occur. If you're opening or closing the window blinds is there anything on the window sill that might consequently fall off, and haphazardly alert someone of a possible local threat that otherwise is not there? Try to feel out every room beforehand as much as possible. If it's a boardroom or frequently used room with lots of people coming in and out then get a feel beforehand by arriving with plenty of time, or on a day prior to your teaching-facilitating day.

Forming Containment Practices

As is with visceral flashbacks, the sense of being able to maintain connection to oneself in the present moment recedes as the felt sense that one is within an overwhelming experience takes over. Rather than the healthy disposition of feeling that one is centered, and connected, and therefore within one's own body, the sense becomes that the crucial happenings in the moment are happening outside of oneself. It's as if one is being pulled around without a say in the decision as to where to go next. If one's movements become jerky, seemingly disconnected from one another, or out of sync, it might be an outward sign that the individual is feeling connected to something other than their present experience and body. Therefore, it is essential to draw attention to the general disposition, without calling out the actual practitioner who is demonstrating the outward signs of disembodiment. In other words, in order to draw attention to the possible inner experience you are observing as a facilitator, we must call upon our shared TCY® intention to honor *through gentle acknowledgment of the indicator of disharmony* versus a desire to fix the physical indicator that is being displayed, so long as it is of non-harm, anatomically-speaking, to them.

How to Teach from a Place of Containment

Whereas the literal dictionary definition of containment is, "The action of keeping something harmful under control or within limits," without a doubt alludes to a negative force, or element, influencing our environment, in the Trauma Cooperative Yoga® classroom sense we are learning to practice energetic, emotional, mental, and physical containment by maintaining a connection to our inner resources as we give of them.

Containment has many functions but to begin let's look at two. Firstly, containment is in relation to how we show up in a yoga classroom. Are we boundaried within ourselves in that we are able to temporarily put aside our personal ideas, and thoughts, and even the details of the day, month, and year? Resting aside the personal details of self in order to best be of service to those in front of us means refraining from even carrying over the residue of the places and moments that we have, or are being influenced by, in that period of our lives.

Teaching a dynamic room of people is challenging enough on its own. The deliverer of the knowledge and ideas is much more sustainable in the pursuit of being a voice and deliverer of information if they have the tenacity inwardly to separate their lives from the life of their work. The 'ten' part of the word tenacity has its etymological roots in the meaning 'to stretch.' We are voluntarily stretching ourselves beyond the limits of our own experiences in order to meet the seeker of your readily made information, the practitioner(s), *without bias.* That takes a considerable amount of containment in one sense of the word.

The second sense of the word we are exploring is the containment of our personal energy selves. In order to restore our personal energy, the practice of containment might look like simply being aware that containment exists as a key tool and dynamic within our teaching practice, and lives as a whole. In the yoga classroom, especially where there is great need, we as teachers are likely to feel obliged to give of ourselves in both small, and large, ways in order to effectively support the possible self-healing that is taking place in the room. Healing in the classroom can look many different ways. We as facilitators are best served to grow as teachers in our teaching skills when we have a grasp on how to contain our energy selves *while holding space for the practitioners before us.*

Some of the ways that we simultaneously hold space for others and practice personal containment of our energy selves is through listening, and practicing presence. Although listening and being present are at least perceived by society to be 'small ways' of giving to those around us, in reality every person, and each trauma survivor, if we check in with ourselves on a personal level, understands that the seemingly small interpersonal acts of being present and listening are quite a blessing to the people in our classrooms. As a wellness facilitator, it is essential to realize that the knowledge of how to maintain self-containment can precede such life changing self-care as the setting of boundaries in our relationships. What we at first establish in our personal lives, in relationship to ourselves and our own needs, ebbs and flows over into our relationships, and entire lives, including the yoga classroom. When we practice maintaining healthy energy selves at home, outside the classroom, we model beyond what words are spoken to our practitioners. Our own self-assigned homework sets a precedence for those looking to us for knowledge, and dedication to the yoga path.

Let's look deeper into boundaries since they support our personal energy and physical containment. Boundaries have many categories including but not limited to the following: spoken and unspoken; physical; time; spatial; emotional, mental, and spiritual. An example of a physical boundary is for instance an ex-husband who will no longer go to their former spouse's home as a meeting place in order to hold their conflict resolution focused conversations. An example of a time boundary is for instance a mother working as a dental receptionist telling her daughter that she cannot speak between 12pm and 12:30pm because those are the first thirty minutes of her lunch break that she needs for self-care such as eating and errands. In reality, yoga takes place both on and off of the mat.

An example of a spatial boundary, for instance, is someone requesting that someone stay on the other side of the table as them and not sit beside them. An example of an emotional boundary can be many things, for instance, if someone has been feeling a lot of anger and is doing their best to shift out of their anger then the individual might very likely choose to take a week away from anyone in their circle who is emitting anger for whatever reason. An example of a mental boundary is a trauma survivor asking friends, family, or their support circle, maybe yoga teacher, not to mention their particular mental trigger in their presence. Finally, an example of a spiritual boundary is a yoga practitioner holding firm that they have the right to be asked beforehand if their yoga teacher plans on using the ancient Reiki symbols directed toward them during final resting posture.

The construction of boundaries are built on self-awareness of how to practice self-containment, just as they might also be founded on the awareness of one's personal triggers. No matter what the reason is for someone to construct a boundary in their lives, it is worthy to mention and realize that the containment of self, and of one's personal resources, is largely reliant on how well someone knows themselves, as well as their own limitations. It is in knowing what best feeds the person's total self, including all aspects of self that are listed above -- such as the mind, body, spirit, and emotional self. As we guide trauma aware yoga classes we thrive, and have the most endurance, as we build and contain our precious inner resources.

This might look a few ways before, during, and after teaching a class:

• Turning off your cell phone a minimum of 30 minutes before beginning to teach so that your mental space is centered in your physical space. • Modeling to practitioners that within 5 minutes of class start time is dedicated meditation time. • Take time to check-in with yourself by pausing in each posture while giving quiet moment invitations to practitioners to recognize the impact of a posture on them, too, whether that be physical, or otherwise. • Choose to teach classes at times of the day that best honor your schedule and fluctuation of energy levels. • Give practitioners a time boundary upon ending class. Say something like, "Today I have 10 minutes after class to connect if anyone has any questions or wants to provide any feedback." • Choose a way you will treat yourself to something nourishing after sharing yourself in such big ways as teaching and leading a class. It might be a meditation practice at home, a special lunch or dinner, a flower-infused bath, a movie, special event, or time to focus on one of your creative projects outside of yoga.

Self-containment also comes into play in the more complex interpersonal areas of our lives. For instance, let's say you really like a new love interest in your life. As the modern saying goes, they "ghost you" and whereas all conversations have been joyful and curious you suddenly stop hearing from them. In hindsight you were giving a considerable amount of energy to anticipating their messages, and the possibility of seeing them again. Now that it seems those possibilities are off the table, you find yourself thinking about them even though the interaction has stopped. The energy of wondering what happened, if in too great a proportion, might carry over into your being available to yourself for the practices that renew you. Therefore, your quality of teaching and personal self-expansion might suffer.

On the other hand, let's say that with the yoga tools you have for use both in your professional and personal life, you choose to listen to these inner curiosities as being perfectly divine as they are. In your perception, they are just prodding you to listen inward deep to what it is you really want. And, in that clarity, aim higher and more resolute in all areas of your life, especially those you have control over. In this case, you might make an agreement with yourself that says that each time you think about this person, you'll make yourself a nourishing treat, or in an inward fashion, notice your body and its energy flow, and in these moments encourage more flow in the stagnant body areas. This decision to practice self-containment instead of giving all your energy away is exactly the healing balm that is needed to rectify a potentially toxic situation into one that feeds you instead of depletes you.

To finish this area of discovery, let's think about how this might apply in the actual yoga classroom. How might a trigger coming from one of your yoga settings, or people within them, only further fasten your sense of self-connection, and therefore self-containment? Let's give the example of the crying practitioner, and the tissue box quick-fix solution. For example, let's say that someone in your class is crying rather unexpectedly. You've never seen them this way. Perhaps your quick reaction is to slide a box of tissues across the floor of the yoga classroom. In reality, you are making their problem yours with your own solution without asking them if it's even an issue for them. Let's say that in this case listening to someone cry personally impacts you, and your sliding the box over makes the practitioner feel uncomfortable.

Instead, as an alternative, you check-in with what's going on for you when you see that person crying. You might just gain back your ground by instead continuing to guide the rest of the class with your returning whole focus by using your ever-strengthening bodily-oriented resolution skills thanks to your TCY practices®. Perhaps, you might share what your body is feeling, in honor of the present moment of the hypothesized crying, *while* then sharing what modification you will do within the posture that you have suggested everyone in the classroom do. This alleviates you from treating the practitioner like a victim, while it also shows them that this practice takes continual effort, and we are all one in our efforts. Their struggle is felt. However, we are also confident as leaders that they will prevail so we continue to pave the way and teach the class.

Work Beyond The 5 Senses: The Interoceptive, Proprioceptive, and Vestibular Systems

Many of us for years as yoga teachers or fitness enthusiasts have been speaking to our classes or peers about becoming aware of where our bodies are in relation to the physical space around us. This is called proprioception. It takes an eagle's eye, and a tiger's focus, to become fully aware of where our body is in relation to all it's parts as well as how each of the parts are interacting and influencing one another. Perhaps, that's why so many of the yoga postures are named after animals! On a factual note, let's look at the roots, or etymology, of the word proprioception. Proprioception is from Latin proprius, meaning "one's own", and capio, capere, "to take, or grasp." What could then be more important to a trauma survivor who has more times than not become disembodied, dissociated, detached, and disconnected from their body and more...than to learn to reconnect to one's body as one's own?

It is so crucial to learn to plug into the power of the physical body because the lack of being aware of where one's body is in space can aggravate the disconnect from one's feelings, and emotions. Oftentimes, people will avoid certain parts of their body, or struggle to move in specific areas of the body, as a byproduct of what we otherwise might call "muscle memory". In reality, the memory is also just as much in the cells throughout the whole body as well as the brain and muscles. So, when we talk about proprioception, we are asking people to come in contact with themselves *and how they are in this world.*

If we can raise our awareness of how our bodies are relating with the space and the world around us, including both animate and inanimate objects, then we might stand a chance through this same cultivated awareness to modify how we show up in the world in relation to others. Proprioception is known as the body's 6th sense after smell, touch, taste, sound, and sight. The body's proprioceptive system sends information to your brain about your body's position in relation to your environment such as how close you are to objects or people around you. The proprioceptive system also communicates back to your brain the amount of effort that is being used to move your body. Additionally, it regulates emotional responses. Can you understand now how crucial it is as a trauma survivor to positively enhance your body's proprioceptive abilities? If you are a trauma survivor yourself you might resonate with the necessity to have a firm grasp on where your body is in relation to others due to this information potentially creating more ease and lessening the number of negative triggers throughout one's day.

The 7th sense is known as the Vestibular System: The vestibular system communicates to the whole of the body through the inner ear. It tells us about our body movement or lack thereof. The vestibular system has a lot of bottom line impact. It helps us coordinate movement, allows us to use both sides of our bodies at the same time, and enables us to remain upright. The vestibular system can be called your body's internal GPS. Here are a few ways that we can encourage the optimal functioning and/or connection to these 2 body systems. Please keep in mind, the following might also serve to encourage further post-trauma integration within the practitioners in your class:

For Proprioception • Give the option to put weighted blankets on the body. • Optional gentle pushing, and pulling, against one's own body, or another's body • Optional squeezing of the body

For Vestibular • Encourage gentle rocking within seated poses • Offer practitioners to swing on a hammock or aerial yoga swing that might be present around the yoga studio • Guide gentle shifting up and down on heels and/or jumping • Practice sliding on floor atop a blanket to feel a sense of playfulness in the body • Suggesting the practice of The Five Tibetans where you incorporate spinning/twirling...

For Interoception aka The 8th Sense In so many words, this is the essence of interoception: our ability to sense ourselves from the inside out through inner body felt experiences. It is key that we therefore honor the practitioners in our classes and/or ourselves as trauma survivors and yoga practitioners when we come up against a moment of felt body intensity. The reality of the body is that it has both conscious and unconscious facets just as the mind does. Therefore, if the body senses danger out of the blue, and alerts the brain, and then the mind, we are ultimately challenged with what to do, and in some cases what not to do.

In a Trauma Cooperative Yoga® setting we are given the environment where rather than trying to fix this noticing of distress in self, or another we are looking to shift the felt experience to one of a new one. Here are some ways to encourage optimal functioning of interoception aka the 8th sense • Practice all forms of meditation • Encourage self and others to stay with all yoga postures as they are being experienced by mindfully responding to inner stimuli in a way that follows what's happening versus ignoring the stimuli • Take notes throughout the mat yoga practice on the feelings you detect in your body in order to increase long term felt awareness • Practice putting your hand over your heart and tapping the floor or chair beside you to mirror the sensed heart rate.

The Four Directions as Mantra in Yoga - Increasing Proprioception Exercise 1

The Four Directions Mantra is a simple reminder to orient oneself to the space around them. Whereas oftentimes people situate themselves in relationship to their environment and then stop there, the four directions mantra is an encouraging reminder to say to oneself in each posture in order to further invite one's connection to their surroundings. The following has examples of how to integrate The Four Directions Mantra by outlining the center of focus as it relates to specific poses. The repeating mantra for The Four Directions is, "Forward, Up, Back, Down." As it is, trauma survivors often feel at a loss when it involves connecting with their environment in a way that engages their strengths. Although these four words, "Forward, Up, Back, Down" are incredibly simple, the felt implication is impactful when one connects the words to the applicational ways the body might adapt to them. As one repeats the mantra to themselves, "Forward, Up, Back, Down", it serves as a grounding force as well as an expansion point as many often feel closed-in by their traumas. Instead of owning our traumas, the trauma owns us, and in an unresolved state dictates whether we feel freedom enough to move in or explore all possible directions of our lives.

Mountain Pose

As one repeats the mantra to themselves, "Forward, Up, Back, Down", one then focuses on the possible implications to this particular posture as the words are spoken silently to oneself. As one focuses on "Forward" it might mean the feeling of the chest moving forward, awareness of the toes facing forward, and perhaps the hands facing forward as fingers extend out in all directions. As the practitioner then focuses on the present interpretation of "Up", it might translate to feeling the upward motion of the chest or sternum, the crown of the head rising up, as well as the internal upward motions of the pelvic floor and the tongue touching the roof of the mouth. In this posture, as the individual allows the focus to shift to the directional cue of “Back”, it might translate to feeling equanimity in the feet as the heels of the feet also press down, the back of the head presses back to encourage the shoulders to rest over the hips. Finally, the back itself is breathed into in order to enhance connection to the indivisible strength of the whole person.

In relation to the “Down” sensation, one might feel the fingertips reaching downward as well as forward, and in this gentle nudge feeling the underarms and shoulder blades reinforce the total strength of the person. These four directions when repeated as a proactive mantra instill a continuous returning to possibility.

Further Implications of This Practice Addition

To have a mudra, or a mantra, to return to is great for cerebral or mental self-discipline. These two yogic practices form the basis for a healthy mind as it is able to transcend certain leanings or tendencies, and override inauthentic cycling of thought, over and over again, to focus on the word or hand gesture that inherently reconnects one to the possibilities of the unique moment. However, to have an inward whole body cue serves to return the practitioner to the innumerable possibilities of discovering oneself as a product of the present. The body and mind naturally stall, and stagnate, in the unconscious desire to retain comfort in the known. However, the dedication within the present to re-experience unlimited possibility keeps us on a positive edge that maintains our connection to self, and therefore calm, while also makes us ever ready to take action in larger than life ways. Again, it is a simple practice, however, it is the essence of larger possibility to stand, sit, kneel, and lie down in a way that serves the resiliency of self in a non-invasive, self-regulated way. *The Four Directions can be used with all postures.*

Cultivate Boundaried Imagery in Class

As Einstein said, ‘Imagination is more important than knowledge. Knowledge is limited.’ This said, in traditional schools we are not taught how to use our imaginations. We might be lucky enough to be taught to express them through fine arts such as painting, drawing, acting, singing, etc. However, there are not many yoga teacher-facilitators yet leading the premise of creativity, or how to use your imagination in classes. This said, as facilitators, we are constantly being asked to improvise even within a pre-planned structured class because of the need to be open to what, or *who*, is in front of us.

It is noteworthy to mention that whereas we might have the best intentions when we suggest that someone imagine themselves on a beach, or overlooking a beautiful sunset, that the same idealistic visions are not going to measure the same or land the same for everyone. Memory is a strong force and influencer on how we relate to imagery in the present-day moment. For instance, *(trigger warning)* if someone watched their father die of a heart attack on the beach during sunset then when they hear the yoga teacher in the room during final resting pose talk about picturing themselves on a beach at sunset it's likely to trigger some awful mind and body felt memories.

So, then, what do we do as TCY® facilitators?

There are so many ways to relate to the shifting of energy in a guided visualization, and that is essentially what we are doing... Let's think for a second of various intentions for why we might have someone visualize imagery in the first place. Here are a few examples:

• To promote a sense of clarity within the practitioner. • To promote a sense of calm within the practitioner. • To encourage the practitioner to move inward. • To strengthen the practitioner's mind and body connection. • To build more helpful mind-body dispositions for the active practice. • To prepare the practitioner for an upcoming exercise or practice. •

So, if not physical imagery, then what is okay?

Author and Founder of *The Lionheart Foundation,* Robin Casarjian is quoted in the book *You The Healer* as saying, "When we visualize we are de-hypnotizing ourselves." That is a powerful statement. First, we as yoga teachers are not the healer, we are however perhaps the channel, guide, and facilitator. The quicker we realize this the slower we are to burnout in the high intensity work that being a yoga facilitator is in fact. *You The Healer* is a book about each one of us being able to heal ourselves. As a certified hypnosis consultant through one of Washington, D.C.'s military Master Sergeants, Jo, also realizes the power of safe wording when giving practitioners the impetus to go within. It is every trauma survivor's hope that we may unburden ourselves from the physically felt echoes of trauma. And, it is every TCY® facilitators' job to provide just that.

In Trauma Cooperative Yoga® it is our duty to resolve to support the survivor's rekindling with the present. However, it is the yoga practitioner's accepted responsibility and positive personal power combined that can support the elimination of constantly living in the past. Trauma survivors may have an occasional reminder here and there of the severe challenges known as trauma that were once enacted in their lives. However, through the practice of yoga it is completely possible that a return to pleasant states of being within the self can begin to enmesh into the survivor's daily life off the mat.

Acceptable Forms of Guided Imagery for Class Visualizations

The human experience is multifaceted and full of dimensions of self that many of us aren't even aware of. Human complexity involves an electromagnetic field aka EMF, too, which holds many various feelings and memories in and of itself. When we meet a real life clairvoyant, seer, or Rishi, as it is called in India, they are often able to see the human electromagnetic field, and all it's colors, and even the quality of the field. This field can also be called 'the aura.' As we guide people through safe visualizations we want to consider the inner felt sense, interoceptive cues, that will impact the aura, or 'vibes', of someone, too. **FYI:** the auric field, or 'light field' around us has been legitimately captured for years by photographic mediums such as Kirlian photography, and Polycontrast Imaging Photography, and pictures of this are searchable online.

More on Self-Containment:

The teaching of containment is inherently an oftentimes frustrating and almost confusing disposition to teach and guide people toward. Therefore, the state of containment must be clearly understood within the practitioner both as the practitioner practices and as they instruct. For the sake of this written guide, we are referring to containment as the inner found center from which one operates while the said individual is also aware of all motions on the axis around them. In order to truly be contained one must know both the physical energies that are around them at any given time. As well as understand how it is that each of these energies has the potential of affecting the self while also remaining to be affected only in ways that benefit the said person of focus. In an overly simplified way, containment is to know and work with the energies present while remaining ultimately connected to oneself.

Shifting into Containment

As you notice the scattered energies of a practitioner in your class, as represented by a lack of self-direction on the mat, it is key to firstly notice how your observation, and the energy behind your personal observation, affects *you.* People, especially the practitioners following along to your guidance, are looking for the truth behind the words. Are you teaching them to care for and listen to themselves? If yes, then, you as a facilitator **must** exhibit genuine signs that you are taking care of you first. This is of course sometimes, especially in the beginning, easier said than done. We live in a world of saving aka "helping" one another. Though, this said, one must be masterful enough to refrain from allowing the noticing of another's disquiet manifested in the physical to become a manifestation in their own experience. On a totally scientific level, our brains lean toward instant emulation, *or mirroring,* of what another in front of us is doing or even feeling. It's the whole, "Monkey-See, Monkey-Do" phenomenon.

People who have geared themselves to the negativity bias by always seeing the negative in people, and the world around them, are less likely to take on someone else's chemical, energetic, or physical disposition only because whether negative or positive they have a deep caution of the world around them ingrained within them. Therefore, facilitators with this disposition are much less likely to struggle with staying grounded in their own experience on the mat from the front of the classroom. However, for everyone else, especially those who are empaths and/or highly sensitive, it takes work and self-reminding to stay steadfast in your commitment to consider your own experience, and how best to cooperate with it in order to lead by example.

Being a facilitator is an enormous, and far more dynamic, role to assume than in a traditional class of teaching to impart knowledge whether it be the benefits of each posture or the anatomically safe approach. Not only are you sharing the benefits and contraindications or warnings of a posture with your class, while demonstrating, or practicing the position, you are considering your own deep inner core needs and observing what might need to be added to the facilitation *without calling anyone out* by name or intense or annoyed staring in order to "help" them understand what they're doing "wrong."

We've really got to trust that the practitioner is okay. If the emphasis is too much on doing it "right" or "wrong" then we are back peddling in the message to trauma survivors to connect with their bodies "as-is", and trust and be patient as their bodies unfurl from tensions and unravel from the stagnant state from which they often tend to exist in life. This connection to the mind and body bridge differs from the awareness of mind only or body only. It is the awareness of the intermingling point of connection itself that determines one's ability to circumvent the body becoming overly influential to the mind or vice versa.

One might say that the body and mind are meant to be seamlessly connected. This is valid as far as the desire to rely on the communication between the two goes. However, in order to view the phenomenon of self-mastery enough as being that one is no longer ruled by the survivor's every outward interaction, or by their every inner shift, or change, it is essential to gain neutrality on the topic of total enmeshment between the two when guiding a classroom. As one slows down their mental noticing, one is able to consequently slow the speed at which one is affected by changes in a bodily sense. Inward psychological and neurochemical changes are often marked or changed by a visceral memory, whether it be old or new. In this case, a visceral change can come about because of re-experiencing the body being reminded by an external felt sense that was known during a past traumatic event.

As we slow down the noticing, we realize we are able to change our experience as our sensing also slows down because we have dedicated ourselves to halting the previously unintentional reactions to external, or internal visceral, stimuli. This goes for both mental and body experience. Let it be known that complete abandonment, avoidance, or ignoring parts of self that one wishes were just not there is far from what is meant to be communicated here. We proceed forward with the desire to know oneself. Not, to cut oneself off from the whole self. So, we may master the self thanks to the slow and methodical practice of yoga.

Cutting off from, ignoring, or avoiding causes fragmentation, and a stifling sense that one simply cannot have key components of self in one's life, due to being perceived as overly challenging, or as unattractive, or undesirable. All parts of self, including previously perceived to be 'shadow' parts of self, are integral to one's learning of self, and therefore both invite and require mastery. In order to truly contain oneself fully we must be willing to embrace rather than deny. We must learn both on and off the mat to balance and even dance between the extremes of self that are a byproduct of the extreme world we live in.

One must be calm enough to be in a place to observe. The calm essence of self only follows the courageous act to face all extremes that arise from within the self. All survivors of trauma have shared bodily, and mental, and emotional experience in the trauma realm and we need to understand that one did not climb the highest peak in one day. Therefore, one cannot expect immediate conquering of all the complexities of self just because one proclaims that one can dance free of pain, struggle, and strife.

As teachers we must learn to gracefully hold space for all perceived-to-be inadequacies. Not only is it true that we magnetize our own states of being by focusing on those very states themselves, but we also energize and therefore attract other people's dispositions depending on how much we are focusing on them, or refraining from doing so. Any meditator knows that the mind itself has varying stages of thought. As we listen closely we learn to listen to the formulation of thoughts before they are even thoughts, and are just feelings or senses. When we know our minds well enough we become clued into what conception of awareness will follow the most recent thought. As we know ourselves, we become more able to anticipate and tolerate our dispositions. This is why the **M.A.T.** process of deep self-consideration every step of the way is essential for the survivor's recovery. This intentional slowing down, and profound self-observation, is what needs to occur in order to best regulate our ability to self-contain.

Both breath, *and awareness,* are bridges to the mind and body total parts of self.

Chapter 9: Successfully Building a Sense of Containment: Security and Safety on The Trauma Cooperative Yoga® mat

In the book, *The Emotionally Connected Classroom: Wellness and The Learning Experience* on page one and six of the introduction the author writes, "In the absence of authentic healthy connections, attachments to unhealthy ones are almost a certainty." And on page six, "Healthy emotional attachments are not taught, they are the product of actual connected emotional experience." As yoga teachers learn to more aptly guide practitioners in the direction of their most true self in each moment in order for ultimate healing to occur it is integral for us to know that everyone is coming from a different emotional landscape. Although what one sees as healthy is true and accurate for one person, it is unknown and unattainable for another unless the healthy emotional landscape is emulated by the practitioner themself as they guide others.

In Chapter One of this same book the author Bill Adair writes about the adaptations necessary for all humankind as we have shifted from our hunter gatherer disposition into classrooms and indoor workplaces. In regards to children in their necessary growth phases the author writes, "Their hunter-gatherer physiology is in a fight for survival, and it is nothing less than a traumatic experience." Similarly, the nervous systems of people who have exited extreme circumstances where taking flight, fighting, or freezing was necessary for survival also exhibit an edginess long after the fact of escaping the original threat. In the author's vision we might even see a certain caginess and combativeness existing within the self of the survivor that is totally unrelated to any present moment reality.

As facilitators in Trauma Cooperative Yoga® it is essential for said guides to become aware of the internal struggle and unprecedented physicalities that the survivor of multiple or intense happenstance or trauma has encountered and might still embody. This is not said to evoke a sense of pity, or extra-weariness, in light of the necessary care and considerations for those rising from unparalleled incidences that the survivor has encountered. On the contrary, all the mentioned considerations brought into this examination are an invitation to discover how to induce a feeling of a welcomed sense of security and safety on the yoga mat for all survivors. Once the yoga facilitator becomes aware of said challenges the prior monochromatic or mono-interpretation, of what orderliness and exactness is becomes rearranged to instead best honor the recovery and perhaps even the speedy recovery of those who are adversely affected by the impact of toxic, abusive, and unsafe environments. Whereas the comforting factor of order is present in the TCY® practice, the order is on the values of the practice versus adhering to strict demands of sequencing particulars.

In *The Emotionally Connected Classroom*, on page four of Chapter One, Adair goes on to emphasize that as the survivor is encouraged to have natural physiological responses and is met in a connected culture within communal safety the body then may return to homeostasis. In the yoga practice space this might look many different ways. Therefore, what does living within one's natural physiological responses look like in the first place? Well, as we might recall the need to sweat, breath heavy or fast, and shake may have been present at the time of initial threat. All things considered, the survivor might encounter similar bodily, emotional, and mental reactions to any perception of threat in the present moment. Yes, even on the yoga mat. Although it might sound counter-intuitive and unlikely for one to feel threatened in an environment that's been created exclusively for the purpose of health and relaxation it is totally normal and natural for the survivor to find themselves in familiar territory within themselves that they didn't necessarily plan to bring to the forefront, especially not in a public or shared setting.

As facilitators it is our responsibility to anticipate uncomfortable sensations to arise for those with whom we share the yoga practice with and to know that at any moment this might be the case. In the realm of comfortability within the survivor this sense of okayness is readily made available when there is a neutral and non-reactionary response, or overly-personalized response, to the yoga practitioner's behavior. In the event of tears shed, due to a practitioner experiencing emotional or mental pain during class time, this might translate to abstaining from sliding a box of tissues across the room, running over to them, or asking if they're 'okay.' Unless the practitioner is requesting specific support such as getting facial tissue then it is suggested to allow people to be in their full self-expression however that might show up from moment to moment. In the spirit of realizing that all physiological responses are normal and natural we as facilitators view all emotional, physical, and mental reactions as being not only okay but encouraged. This is of course within reason in that so long as all responses are nonviolent they are acceptable.

It is pertinent to be a container of acceptance and compassion for all yoga practitioners that are before you as a yoga facilitator. If one senses their ability to be as they are is respected and even cared for in a healthy and boundaried way then the practitioner's physiology will more readily shed it's impediments in the form of toxins stored. Crying, shaking, rocking, note taking, clearing one's throat or nasal passageways, being still, repeating a motion numerous times, or quietly walking out of the room are all ways to discharge the sense of latent threat within the body, mind, spirit, emotional and spiritual self. Staring off in space and closing one's eyes is even acceptable. Although the yoga teacher might see this as a form of disconnect and disembodiment if tended to delicately and with the introduction of said mannerism as a strength then the practitioner is more apt to recognize the response and direct or embody it as one that is advantageous for whole self health and recovery.

THE ESSENCE OF CONTAINMENT

At the heart of the work of containment is the ability to, "hold opposite truth." Being overly attached to any one reality as poised by one's mind or as presented by another is both ungrounding and short-lived. Extremes, extremist personalities, extremist sports and the like, all burn out before too long. The body, mind, and emotional self can only maintain an exact frequency for so long. No one can be sad nor happy forever, and neither can one stay upright forever. In the search for equilibrium, peace, and well-being such desirable states are also fleeting. Yet, people continue to strive forward, nations continue to form, and communities on and off the yoga mat manage to heal. Therefore, we might derive from this vantage point that containment is based upon the ability to thrive in many terrains and within many dispositions on both large and definite scales. Yoga is for this reason very popular in that within the extreme moments demanding of us exertion, focus, and flexibility there is an acceptance of where one is at within each practiced, or newly-visited place. It is within this acceptance that one is more readily able to preside over what-is, without flickering out in their original intention, or aim. Or, more succinctly put, is able to contain oneself within the present pull of reality.

So, what does it look like to "hold the opposite truth" in the framework of the yoga classroom? And, what does 'opposite truth' even mean in this context? Here is a writing exercise that may serve to demonstrate how one may actively observe what-is while also inviting what might be albeit what one might become is incredibly different than what one is at present. Although the watchful yoga practitioner may observe this so-called evolution of self on the yoga mat it is often unheard of for a yoga practitioner to both be encouraged and to proactively seek to be at one with oneself throughout the process of said evolution by way of including mindful mental engagement.

The following exercise requires thoughtful focus on three of the major brain centers mentioned throughout this body of work. As well as, a pen and paper and a relatively quiet space within which one might be comfortable enough to move freely within for as far as one may comfortably reach outward with their toes and fingers in all directions. If you're looking for a vision in your mind then think The Vitruvian Man in which Leonardo da Vinci drew a symbolic sketch of what he believed to be an illustration of the divine connection between the human body and the universe. With this consideration in mind we might admire the thoughtful creation that we are all a part of.

BEGIN MIND PRESENCING EXERCISE

STEP 1: Write down one thing you notice about your body that feels very real and noticeable.

STEP 2: Write the words, "Yes, and?"

STEP 3: Below this write the next thought that comes to mind.

STEP 4: Continue steps 2 and 3 for as long as one more page in writing while simply observing what is present within your awareness of self.

STEP 5: Challenge your original statement of bodily self-awareness by writing down the answer to what you think that part of your body or self needs. It might be a direct bodily statement such as, "I need to stretch." Or, it might be a solution that is seemingly unrelated to the body however that arises as you ask yourself what the original area of focus requires. For example: "I need to accept my part in the current situation that is going on." Perhaps the sentence expands or perhaps it is complete as it reads in the above. Note: This part of the exercise is to mindfully engage one's present moment needs.

STEP 6: Next, write down the words "YES, AND?" again.

STEP 7: Respond with how you might actively self-soothe at this stage of your self-discovery process.

STEP 8: Next, write "Yes, and?" once again.

STEP 9: Write the words, "I am ready to take action now."

STEP 10: Take thoughtful action to work toward both acknowledging what-is while also making way for what might become once you have taken action. **For example:** if you feel a manageable level of discomfort in an area of your body, then breathe into and meditate inwardly on the surrounding areas, and body as a whole, to determine where either the source of the discomfort is coming from or what area of the body you want to actively feel into in order to mindfully stretch and move into it.

STEP 11: Write down the phrase, "Yes, and?" before then responding with how you observe yourself, in any or all ways including mentally, physically, emotionally, or spiritually, now that you've taken a bold initiative by following these steps *without expectation* for anything to immediately change within, or outside, of the self.

In order to effectively practice self-containment we must be willing to both see ourselves as how we are and how we want to be long term. Containment is the ability to hold opposites. It is within the willingness to engage oneself as oneself is not as one wishes for oneself to be.

This exercise requires one to have a secure base in order to have the ability to feel safe and secure enough to self-discover. Just as when children develop trust in the availability and reliability of their primary relationship their anxiety is then reduced, as The University of East Anglia points to and as inspired by John Bowlby's theory of attachment, the facilitator therefore is the primary reference point for each practitioner in the classroom. This intrinsic component of the facilitator-practitioner relationship is ever present in the yoga classroom. Rather than the facilitator walking around the room to tirelessly check the practitioners' posture the facilitator is asked to stay reliable by maintaining a continuous position at the front of the room. Rather than logging how the practitioners are showing up in the postures with the mind to correct how they embody the posture, *with the caveat of the mentioning of harm prevention in each posture,* the facilitator embodies options and variances that move beyond mere stagnation within one posture once the posture's form is attained in accordance with age old books.

Finding security and safety in each posture looks different in accordance to not only the physical abilities of the practitioner but the emotional, mental, and energetic contributions that each practitioner brings to the mat. The University of Anglia also points out that our secure base shifts as we become adults to rely on secure adult relationships that consistently offer comfort and reassurance. In universal lineages of thought it might be believed that by sharing one's own experience other people then feel beneficially comforted. Although it is not the job of a yoga facilitator to divulge their entire life it is advantageous to share cornerstones of 'the general why' behind actions or inactions in the name of building trust, consistency, reliability, and common ground that in part further encourages feelings of safety and security. In fact, in the Greater Good Magazine as published by The Greater Good Science Center of UC Berkeley studies published in the journal SCAN emphasize findings that just by knowing an experience is shared with another reward parts of the brain are then inherently lit up therefore producing feelings of wellness. Surely, one feels safer and more secure knowing they are not alone in the depths of an experience.

DIVULGING THE GENERAL WHY

Now that there is evidence of the positive impact of sharing what one is experiencing with another, or in this case the yoga classroom, in order to build trust, security, and safety within the community let's explore why it's key to even emphasize positive psychology to begin with. The Harvard Business Review published an article called *Calming Your Brain During Conflict.* Before we explore this topic more please remember that although there is no visible threat present for yoga practitioners in the safe haven of a professional and morally-grounded practice studio the internal body cues might and often do suggest otherwise. Therefore, enacting as much positive reinforcement is integral to navigating the Trauma Cooperative Yoga® classroom. This said, let us continue.

Scientifically, when the human brain's amygdala goes off due to perceived threat whether real or remembered within the yoga practitioner's mind at the time of practice, the prefrontal cortex is impeded in it's functioning. This means that complex thinking is out the window and so is decision making. Therefore, if one is able to observe a yoga practitioner in possible distress, while embodying one's own practice as the yoga facilitator, while simultaneously offering up what one observes as the yoga facilitator within their own self, and give a neutral statement as to what might encourage the *best yoga practice experience* for the practitioner before them, it is beneficial in the facilitator and client-practitioner relationship. One, the practitioner in possible distress feels less threatened by someone else speculating about them, or their state of being, because the language that is coming from the facilitator is "I" centered. The "I" inclusion is sincere, and shares what the facilitator is comfortable sharing about their practice choices and practice limitations. While, secondly, trust is built as the facilitator gives a probable circumstance of what one might try "if they're experiencing" X, Y, or Z. The findings observed and vocalized by the facilitator not only reflect the possible state that is being embodied by the practitioner yet also is inclusive of one's own personal journey. Thus, normalization is embodied and enacted.

In this case, the words, "It's okay if you're feeling X, Y, Z." are effectively unnecessary. For example, "It's okay if you're feeling tired, upset, impatient. All of which are 'finalistic projections' by the facilitator. Instead, the sure fire truth is revealed in that the facilitator is a vocalized, and normalized, human being who is also having their own journey, and is functioning enough, and ambitious enough, in one's own recovery to have the peace of mind to pursue knowledge for the sake of not only their own recovery, but for the recovery of the people in their classroom, too. In effect, recovery for one, as one is all, and all is one. So, then how far is it okay to share and to what extent is it advised to share one's life in the cultivation of a safe and secure space for all in the yoga classroom? Rather than going into details as to how the teacher-practitioner has come to having a discomfort, or malady, in the bodily, emotional, or physical capacity, saying a quick one liner, such as "Due to my current life experiences," or, "Due to my current home environment," I am choosing to focus on this part of the posture. However, you might be best served to focus on the elongation of "X", or stillness in the "Y" region as a way to honor what's happening within you and your practice.

THE NITTY GRITTY OVERHAUL

Many times we as people will hear the general reproach to "be nice." Some people might even have heard this when they themselves truly thought they were in fact "being nice." Yet, the felt sense of someone being nice or not is reliant on one's present day felt sense of the moment, too. Therefore, no matter what is sometimes said by a yoga facilitator it might land with the yoga practitioner in such a way that startles or annoys them for whatever reason. There is the general idea of all people that we deserve to be liked as people for who we are as people. Yet, a day in ordinary life shows that this is far from the experience for everyone on the face of the planet. Not everyone is liked, in fact no one is liked by all.

As a yoga facilitator it is perhaps most easy to fall behind the knowledge of general anatomy and therefore speak of nothing but anatomy for most if not all of the class. For those teachers who use anatomy as a central theme this desire to educate is admirable. However, it is not what a facilitator does by any right. A facilitator induces knowing within the practitioner by following the emphasis of the M.A.T. process. As the facilitator reminds the practitioner that it is not only okay to inquire of and listen to one's inner needs, in new ways other than perhaps the way one has listened before, and it is an expected part of the process within the yoga class, as it unfolds, it becomes second nature to more deeply learn what is needed on one's mat for the self. The practitioner therefore may or may not know the name of the bone or minor and major muscles groups being worked within however they know the feeling of what is being worked and therefore are aware of how much longer or shorter a period to stay in that posture for their own sense of wellness as well as whether or not they need to return to a posture that works the same area of the body, or not, in the remaining class time.

The shifting away from constant anatomical reference, traditional flow sequencing, or posture exactness as was initially taught by the yoga gurus of India for the male population, as the primary focus, can be somewhat unnerving for many if not all yoga teachers. The primary focus as TCY® practitioners that we are focusing on shifting toward is moving more freely within the preliminary safety concepts of each posture, listening more deeply as we follow the M.A.T. process, and practicing within a greater range of choice. In the name of union, of all parts of self, and trust in the innate knowing *of not only our own bodies as facilitators but of those of the practitioners,* we shift toward facilitating rather than just regurgitating what has been taught to us. The next question or concern that often arises next is how can one feel safe not giving exact instructions that they in turn expect the practitioners to then embody themselves. The answer is found within the **M.A.T.** guiding principle. People only know what they know about themselves. People have a direct relationship within themselves unlike any other person, onlooker, or superbly-trained teacher of ancient asana.

Of course, as yoga teachers we are told to encourage whatever variation of each posture it is that best suits each practitioner whether it be the 'beginners', 'intermediate', and 'advanced' options. As teachers we effectively know the benefits and contraindications of the postures. However, what if that posture altogether is a disservice to the practitioner due to the mental, physical, emotional make up of said proposed practitioner? Every day is different. And, every day presents its own obstacles and nuances. Furthermore, who is to say that someone who is capable of doing an advanced version needn't retire the advanced expression of that posture for a day for the sake of one practice flow in order to best honor what is happening on that day for them on an anatomical level, or the proposed emotional, or mental levels? Why then, is it called "beginners, intermediate, advanced"?

As teachers we know to invite people to go to downward facing dog or resting pose.

As facilitators we know the natural inner dispositions that might occur as a byproduct of moving energy around into areas of the body that the practitioner might've entirely disembodied long ago. As facilitators we know that there is no need to apply hands to a practitioner in order to make the posture look as it does when one has finally arrived at the posture's 'ultimate expression' in your own body. As a facilitator, we know that solutions occur within when one listens enough and is therefore given the chance to listen deeply enough to the natural occurrences within. As facilitators of TCY® we know that offering up what is happening within the self as a facilitator, in a calm manner might awaken greater self-tolerance, and self-compassion, within the practitioners before us. We know that our courage and willingness to stay present with what-is goes hand-in-hand with the next step of offering up what we as facilitators are going to sequentially do next in order to self-soothe, and take initiative, to create change in the modeling of life in its most honest form, the human body, at the front of the room. In short, the facilitator shares their own inner dialog in a succinct, and not overly-indulgent way, while offering up exact insight into 2-3 other options of how to embody the posture depending on what is bodily-observed within the practitioner(s) before them. This works with both private sessions, and in group class.

PEOPLE PLEASING STUNTS GROWTH

In Psych Central online Sharon Martin wrote an article saying that people-pleasing is a byproduct of the "fear of rejection, abandonment, conflict or criticism". Let's put it like this though: if we as yoga teachers, or facilitators, allow our fear of any of the above to reign in our minds then we lose the quality of our contribution to the people whom we serve on the yoga mat. In fact, healthy psychological containment is predicated on our ability to set out for our proverbial golden seas beyond the possible threats of being rejected by those newcomers we might pass along the way, of the fear of being abandoned by our tribe, of being in conflict with ourselves or others, or fear of being stymied by potential outside criticism. When we recognize any of these arising within us we must as facilitators use the inner resources available to us and as presented by this body of work.

This same article reminds readers that, "You can't remain a healthy, patient, kind, energetic, caring person if you constantly give but never replenish your (own) needs." The meeting of needs is embedded in the very framework of the practice and revisited many times over throughout the course of one's practice. Behaviors become a part of us through our own self-engrained repetition. If we as facilitators show through our repetitive actions that we include our own selves into the very consideration of each step along the way in the practice then we are creating regular occurrences of modeled self-regulation through self-acknowledgement on a ***whole self* scale.** The conversation ceases to be about physical considerations alone but of the very inner framework that arranges for the physical to take place.

When we think about the inner-infrastructure of the self in this context of the yoga classroom it is not just about meeting whims, feelings, or pre-calculated movements. Yet, it is about the meeting of all of the self as we are while being aware of our best case scenario. In the divine pursuit of our ever-evolving self what kind of people do we want to be both on and off the mat? Do we want to be blind followers of history? Under what circumstances are we to pursue the becoming of the vision we have in our mind's eye? And, how is one ready enough to act large in one's life off the mat if one is going unnoticed-by-self on the mat? What parts of self do we need to consider in everyday life? And, do they have a place on the yoga mat? How do we safely and tenderly bring all parts of self to the forefront of our awareness, and in respectful acknowledgment? The answer is we need to dive yet more *inwardly* to discover how we want all parts of self to unfold, and impact our bodies, and on our lives off the mat. Might it be said that the yoga mat is an optimal training ground to reshape bodily, mental, and emotional responses?

On another note.

What needs of ours are valid? What needs of ours can we hold space for and contain within the framework of sharing ourselves and our lives on the mat through the noticeably self-prescribed movements, or absence of movement, in the TCY® classroom? How do we become self-directing practitioners of yoga and life while honoring and including all life forms around us including the human ones on our shared path? Finally, in what environment can we contain our own inner-direction and self-regeneration while enjoying the company of a full classroom and the guidance of the leading facilitator present?

In TCY® we aim to explore our inner assets of courage to explore what we need in the present moment albeit the need might look very different from the representation of the needs of the person beside us. The practitioner peer beside us might be pursuing a whole different path of physical expression altogether. And, that's okay. This is okay because the facilitator-practitioner at the front of the room is lending space, trust, and confidence enough in the practitioners present to embolden freedom of choice even when it comes to postures to be practiced.

The essence of containment is to approach oneself as one is without resistance but with considerate restraint. Authenticity is described by Stephen Joseph in Psychology Today as "being true to yourself and experiencing yourself as behaving in accordance with your true thoughts, beliefs, personality, or values." By this definition alone it is difficult to guess how authenticity might transfer to the yoga mat considering yoga is oftentimes a physical vehicle of self-expression. However, given that the same article by Joseph, *"Why Being Yourself Matters"*, also says that authenticity is a key to happiness it seems well worth the mental exertion to find out how it might cross over into the practitioner's life on the yoga mat. TCY® is asking you to think more deeply and listen more deeply to what is being called for in the wholing and uniting of full self. Or, as the ancient yogis said in the still relevant texts today, "yolking", as it means union.

How often have we shut off the calls from within for the sake of following a protocol outlined by someone existing outside of the greatest origin of authenticity itself: *The Self?* Unfortunately, in many yoga classes the world over, although the teacher's words are an invitation to only do what you can and to feel comfortable doing "a lesser version", or "more beginner version", the invitation to direct one's physical self as they wish is oftentimes on deaf ears. Although in TCY® the practitioner does have many suggestions as to what one might do next so that one feels far from lost, or at a loss, as to "what to do", from the initial suggestion, there are different ways to inhabit each posture because different people are going to need different dynamics of the posture. The added layer of encouraged self-assessment with the M.A.T. principles is an extra bonus for all the practitioners in the room.

When people enter a classroom together there is often a reminder from the teacher to please not pay attention to the people to your left and right. "This is no competition." Although this is a lovely idea the invitation is coupled with oftentimes strenuous instructions coming from a teacher who receives pay based on how happy the yoga practitioners are with the degree of physical challenge they were given that day in class. Yet, there are classes filled with practitioners who are curious to practice in such a way that invites self-direction, self-inquiry, and self-discovery in the face of prompted healthy self-assertion. As a TCY® facilitator these are your people, and it is your work to repeatedly show them how natural and healthy it is to do each of these self-study practices as mentioned. Furthermore, might practitioners start practicing on their lunch break for 10 minutes, or integrating yoga into their daily lives more often, when the approach is equally as inner-guided? If it is not guarded as being a source of knowledge that is only able to be incarnated by those who have gone through the rigorous rite of passage of yoga teacher training itself then isn't there a greater sense of cultivated oneness in that open sharing? What are teachers possibly missing out on by taking a stance of being all-knowing, and refraining from sharing how they come to arrive in each posture in their practice? Is there a false sense of command or hierarchy being created by refraining from trying on these new practices of M.A.T.?

Chapter 10: Breath Mastery as an Integral Part of Self-Healing

The breath is a refuge in all points of life. In Trauma Cooperative Yoga® such as in life the quick and accurate assessment is that attention loses lustre in all things but the breath itself. Toys, accolades, even voyages and trips on the vast earthly plane where we live all lose their shine and attention-absorbing power over time. The breath is an endless grounding force, an anchor, and an uplifting force for mood and mental stamina. The breath even influences mental, bodily, and sexual outcomes. All of these life areas impact whether or not we are a success personally and professionally.

When we talk with people we often without conscious awareness watch how they breathe. Is the breath moving through the mouth, the nose, or both? Where does the breath land in the body? In other words, where do we see a person's body or our own bodies as the breath circulates in the body over a matter of seconds or minutes? The Greater Good Science Center magazine produced by The University of California, Berkeley writes about what focusing on the breath does for the human brain. The article talks about how the brain stem is by far the only influencer or producer responsible for the breath cycles. It concludes that fast breathing, oftentimes known to yoga practitioners as the breath of fire, "increases activity in the amygdala" and "may trigger feelings like anxiety, anger, or fear." For someone with a settled nervous system unaffected by the extremes of traumatic life events this breath is often practiced with little negative side effects. However, with someone with an amped central nervous system (more on this in chapter 14) due to unprocessed trauma the requirement of such a breathing practice is of little to no beneficial gain for the practitioner and might even cause harm.

Please realize that the words, 'for those unaffected by traumatic life events' far from implies that some people just don't experience trauma. Because we all do. However, people's social support networks and general lifestyle and habits impact the body, mind, and emotional systems ability to process the life events of a traumatic kind. The amygdala isn't a bad word nor a part of the brain to be fearful of. On the contrary, if listening to resources such as Sounds True podcasts and their elite gathering of neuroscientists interviewed by the host, Tami Simon, you might learn that by 'talking to your amygdala' with affirmations and initial awareness of the location of the brain region that encases the 'walnut-sized brain area', as many resources including the American Psychological Association relate to it as being, the amygdala itself will calm down. This can return the trauma survivor to a place of manageability within the self. Of course, in order to have the awareness of self to harness the presence of mind to tend to a more difficult personal moment we oftentimes require the steadiness of the breath. With practice, the two requisites of mindfulness and the actual physical practice of the direction of breath become second nature.

Then, do breath changes start in the body or the mind? The breath is something that is always with us so long as we are all alive. This is rudimentary information that we've all been born with from day one. So why then put so much emphasis on its origins in the first place? For the trauma survivor whether in a yoga class or outside of the yoga practice space mere attention to the breath can cause unrivaled anxiety and feelings of unease. Languaging principles such as do we bring attention 'on' the breath or 'to' the breath can bottomline the main source of contention that evolves from the breath focus for so many. Perhaps you have been speaking with a loved one and you suggest to them that they 'just breathe' or 'just focus on their breath'. This can elicit all sorts of responses from gratitude for the reminder to haste for assuming the person isn't already breathing or doing their best within their own natural breathing flow. Pay close attention to the difference for a moment.

"Please bring your attention *in*to the experience of your breath".

Or,

"Please bring your attention onto your breath."

One is a receptive cue to awaken connection. When we come to or toward something we genuinely want to meet it for whatever purpose or agenda may be the cause. Whereas when we bring our attention onto something there's a sense of moving above or domineering it. Think about it. We place our hand onto something. We move onto something else to do usually with a sense of positive assertion. In all things, positive self-assertion is a beneficial trait. Yet, when it comes to breath, something that is a life of its own, and oftentimes follows impulse aka the environmentally caused quick need for reaction the breath often changes before our mind or awareness does. This is why listening to our breath instead of trying to commandeer it is essential to realizing effective change moment to moment.

However, on the flip side, when people are asked to change their breath in any way other than it is in the moment the effect can often be to escape into one's mind. Self-consciousness becomes a key factor of one's experience, and the breath often moves upward into the chest. The autonomic nervous system switches to self-preservation mode, quickening the heart, and activating the sense that something or everything needs to be different than it is. It's at this point that the experiencer of the moment can feel alienated from one's own body and freezing or fleeing from the present moment is more likely than actively facing the moment head on as a learning experience. When one is safe or perhaps most importantly *feels* safe the person is more likely to stay grounded and discover what the moment has to offer.

The breath, self-awareness, mental activity resulting in self-realization and the body's state of operation are all inextricably linked for better or worse. The impact of this information all has to do with how the reader decides to interpret the science. No one is bulletproof to being affected by life. In fact, being moved by our circumstances, and desires, to take control and action are all superhuman traits. Yet, what the brain and mind needs to realize is when to back down so that the body can support the two in regulating in order for the brain and mind to come back stronger than before with newfound realization as to how to handle each situation as it arises.

Knowing what we know now, it is pertinent to recognize that both refraining from certain breath patterns and by noticing the impact of life's many surprise scenarios on the body *as soon as possible* the positive personal power trio of mind, body, breath can advance one's ability to manage and ultimately self-recover. As Healthline is quoted in writing, "The amygdala disables the frontal lobes and activates the fight-or-flight response." Then, goes on to say, "Without the frontal lobes, you can't think clearly, make rational decisions, or control your responses." Although we started off talking about and indeed are still talking about the power of the breath and its role in our lives, we are led to the whole neurophysiology behind the extraordinary occurrence that is our breath. In resolve, Trauma Cooperative Yoga ® stands behind the core sentiment of the practice of self-recovery through traumatic times, *"Attention loses its lustre in all things but the breath."*

These words on this page are but words. They are signposts toward your own realizations about your own breath. They are anchors for your continued dedication to unraveling the blocks and hindrances, the liberators and allowers, of your own unrestricted flow of breath. Every human on the planet knows the restraints of the breath as well as the glories and joy of it as it arises without tedious effort. The natural reacclimation to the healthy self that occurs when the breath is free to roam as it does, unrefined by the shoulds and shouldn'ts, is beyond words powerful. In this acclimation to the capable self, the mind is calm, the brain is nourished, and the body is met with balance.

THE WONDERS OF BREATH

Andrea Gibson writes:
"...and I wonder if Beethoven held his breath
the first time his fingers touched the keys
the same way a soldier holds his breath

the first time his finger clicks the trigger.

We all have different reasons for forgetting to breathe."

Whereas this is beautiful, relevant, and thoughtful writing as it is inclusive of so many human life experiences we must remember as yogis that our bodies never forget to breathe. They pause because they are overwhelmed. They pause because they do not want to be seeing what they are seeing. They pause because they have perhaps asked us to do the same.

In a self-perfecting culture set on making what is wrong right the crux of the matter can subside in our awareness of self. The matter is not that the breath of our bodies ceased momentarily to flow as we think it should. The central key point is that we are being turned toward ourselves in that emptiness of breath. We are perhaps being asked to empty ourselves of what we think we should be doing or might want to do about what is happening and instead do what must be done. Our highest calling in life, and in a TCY® setting, is not to instruct people on how to live perfectly, or never miss a beat, but how to fill the moment of realizing a part of ourselves has stopped beating, whether it be breath or purpose. Will we try to correct ourselves for the inevitable change in course, rhythm, and tone of our lives? Or, will we allow with grace what is trying to be uncovered?

As the first article in this breath section pointed out, the breath comes from more places than just the brain stem. The brain stem is our sensing. The brain stem might not be the most recent 'higher' brain development through time that is our frontal lobe but it knows unequivocally that life is happening to us in every pulsing moment. Will we listen to the invitation to reset? Will we fill the temporary void of breath with gentle reassurance that we were here all along waiting for this new moment to start? As we go to reinitiate our depth of breath again centered low in our bellies will we allow ourselves to accept the absence as an integral part of us? Must we always be in flow?

As Alexander Lowen says in his book, *The Voice of the Body,* "The importance of breathing need hardly be stressed. It provides the oxygen for the metabolic processes; literally it supports the fires of life. But breath as pneuma is also the spirit or soul. We live in an ocean of air like fish in a body of water. By our breathing we are attuned to our atmosphere. If we inhibit our breathing we isolate ourselves from the medium in which we exist." That is why breathing is the dominant factor in the practice of Yoga." But, what is "pneuma" and how do we stop the inhibition of our breath? Pneuma is 'air in motion', 'breath', or 'soul.' Its roots are in Greek culture and can also boil down to the meaning, "spirit of a person". Alexander Lowen's life experience points once again to the reasoning and call to action for every living being to stop judging their breath as something that needs to be controlled or fixed.

The breath is to be invited into existence through one's own close observation and not possessed. However, as Lowen also points out there are physical markers that one might anticipate such as the gentle rocking back of the pelvis at the inhalation's start and the lifting up of the chin as the breath carries through the body. Outside of consistencies though there lies discovery and possibility for new felt sense. As the body feels new connections within it the mind and the spirit are more deeply touched and the breath therefore even more deeply reinvigorated. The cycle of interconnection within the self follows and this same self, independent yet universally shared by all, is encouraged to seek external landscapes that mirror the new inner sense of connection. Bridges are formed, and bonds are forged.

A Deep Dive into Breath

"What we need is ambition and intention. What to do is then easy." – Malala

The following quote is from the book Trauma and Memory: Brain and Body in A Search For The Living Past, A Practical Guide for Understanding and Working with Traumatic Memory by Peter Levine. It speaks to the voluminous, and ever-shifting, relationship to breath that we all have. In this part Dr. Levine talks of working with survivors in his practice, "Asking them to focus on their breath may precipitate a panic reaction; simply requesting that they keep still often only increases their agitation." (where agitation is present.) Whereas we do not forego the yogic focus of breath completely, in the practice of Trauma Cooperative Yoga®, we instead might suggest that the practicing practitioner before us is guided to become aware of and notice their breath. As well as, to allow the breath to be as it is while encouraging self-expansion through greater connection. One of the main ills of being traumatized is that our world both inner and outer become restricted and unmoving. On the contrary, as far as breath modulation is concerned, and its parameters, in teaching to people who do not identify as trauma-affected, we give exact breath cues.

The exactness of breath instruction in a so-called general public class, although we are routinely made aware that the trauma affected state runs in more survivors than not, varies greatly. In the event that we are being asked to focus on our breath in such a way that sounds forceful, or coincides with a high expectancy to yield a specific outcome, we as survivors likely may become triggered. One of the primary causes of this unnecessary form of triggering is that survivors have a difficult enough time being open to observing themselves. Therefore, making it overly obvious that you're probing into their inner state, coupled with desiring to feel, act, or straight up be different, is a recipe for disturbance within the survivor.

Seeing Triggers as a Blessing

On the flipside, when we tiptoe around survivors of great trauma, especially those who are looking to us for relief, in our Trauma Cooperative Yoga® setting, we send the message that we see the practicing practitioner before us as potentially or very broken. Survivors affected by trauma, and living in Post Traumatic Stress, are stronger than most. It is our duty to speak to the survivor and the warrior within them. Not, the victim, or victimized. This looks many different ways. We will continue to cover the details of language throughout this book. Peter Levine, also in his book, *Trauma and Memory,* is opened by a foreword by Bessel van der Kolk, that says "Negative judgment of oneself or others causes minds and bodies to tense up, which renders learning impossible." And continues to say, in regard to the brain relationship in connection to this body and mind predicament, the following, "The (key) areas of the brain that are devoted to self-awareness, as in the medial prefrontal cortex, and body awareness, as in the insula, often are shrunk in people with chronic Post Traumatic Stress. The body, mind, and brain have learned to shut down."

Therefore, the above quote further illustrates the alienation that might occur if you directly insinuate any one way to move, or breathe, as being the best or only way. Finally, in the opening of Dr. Peter Levine's book, Van der Kolk writes, "In order to recover, people need to feel free to explore and learn new ways to move. Only then can nervous systems reorganize themselves and new patterns be formed. This can only be done by investigating new ways of moving, breathing, and engaging, and cannot be accomplished by prescribing specific actions at fixing." The further encouraging news for any trauma survivor is that, "Attention to internal experiences uncovers procedural movements that tend to be unintentional and reflexive."

As we are made, almost too well aware, we do not choose to put our attention on flashbacks or triggers, yet they just happen. However, Yoga, Meditation, Hypnosis, Prolonged Exposure, EMDR, and psychodynamic therapies all center on being made aware in a life empowering way. The gathering of new awareness, through introspection, builds the potential for long-standing stamina and habitual resilience. When we can learn to guard our noticing with receptivity based on self-confidence then we can overcome it. Of course, firstly must come the vision of overcoming.

Therefore, as facilitators, when we encourage people to feel into their successes, to notice the depth of their inner encouraged, and inner found, success we further imprint the evolution of future body and mind success. Not only do deeply felt body feelings drive everything in our physical, day-to-day, lives but they also drive our courage on the mat, too. The courage to explore beyond what one knows, or directly hears, is the basis for recovery from overwhelming, or chronic, Post Traumatic Stress. The root of self-discovery is the freedom to find yourself anew.

Triggers as Neutral Spots in Mind and Body

The problem with newfound body awareness is that it often becomes feared as triggers are perceived as demoralizing to the desire to be an unconquerable self, and because we avoid being triggered so much, we become each trigger's ultimate prey. Whereas we as teachers work to reduce negatively impacting people through our own words, actions, and intentions, we must be made ultimately aware that triggers will happen. As we learn to dissect our own contributions to unnecessary suffering, we become more alive through our own energy-giving learning curves. When we show the ways of the warrior, as we practice transparency, through our own divulging of our own inner process we light the way for the practitioner to reveal themselves to the most important observer yet . . . *themselves.*

As we embolden survivors to stay in connection to their inner awakenings, through remaining to be attentive to muscular, tissue, and organ felt changes--such as heart and breath rhythms, or the stomach's processing or sounds being made--we become stronger as people, and anchors for survivors in healing, and in general, as teachers. We recognize the spirit of possibility within ourselves, and others, as a sign that the practitioner might be able to shift their felt experiences, in noticing and remaining connected to the temporary nature of all feelings, whether emotional or physical.

Remaining Connected to Calm

As in every other activity, practiced by humans, one might become competitive with one's self, in a way that potentially errs on the side of causing self-harm in the classroom practice. In answer to this, so long as we are encouraging people to feel into their triggers, versus engaging them through beginning to live their story, we have done our job as teachers. Please remember that people will always do what they want to do no matter how hard we try to liberate them from stale repetitions of yesterday's understanding. Or, innerstanding for that matter. However, when they are coming to you as a teacher, they are meant to sense that there are indeed other ways of being, outside of the longtime lived version they've begun to cling to in hopes of avoiding being triggered themselves.

What Happens When Triggers Become Anger

A popular term in today's world is Anger Management. However, for the sake of being informed as Trauma Cooperative Yoga® facilitators, we might consider that managing implies on some level(s) controlling. In order to control one's anger, one usually works to squash the sensations of anger, in the body, as well as the mind's thoughts. The objective is instead to redirect our thoughts that are born as a byproduct from our most recent trigger, to ones that stem from a genuine noticing in the present moment of the pain associated with that trigger. Pain is with us all day long, in the back of our minds, and sometimes in the complexities of our bodies. Only, we often do not recognize pain because our survival instincts are at work, to keep us alive, and essentially taken care of. A great example of this non-realizing of pain, is when you go into receive a massage, and although you're more relaxed than you've been in awhile, you notice pain where you didn't realize there was any. Neuromuscular massage therapists have also been known to educate their clients on the idea that unexpected laughter, when receiving massage, is the body's coping, or reflex, to latent discomfort, as well as pain, that's been sitting in the body. Hence, the drawing away from the cause of the sensation is a bodily defense mechanism to deter further exploration of the discomfort and/or pain.

So, why are we exploring the body's potential manifestations of discomfort, and pain, in the first place? Because our own pain and anger is best when not addressed from a control standpoint of so-called managing. If we are looking for total freedom as evolving yoga practitioners, sharing in the practice, then we might be best served to view anger as an alliance in the self-healing process. We manage our classrooms, we manage our interaction with our practitioners who are hungry to learn. We manage our lives with our employees, children, and pets. Anger, itself, is an internal process that is undeniably a part of ourselves, no matter who evolved we are, or how much time we've spent at mindful self-evolution. In the healthiest internal world possible, we learn to communicate with our alliances. Once we have done so, we functionally express our anger as an internal agent of change.

Chapter 11: Transparency of Experience

In the traditional yoga setting, practitioners enter the classroom to learn everything they can from the guide, or facilitator. In the most conducive learning environments such practitioners show up with plenty of mental space to directly experience the teaching ways of the class leader. In the most altruistic settings, the teacher in turns empties themselves of all the knowledge they possess, from both their former training and their own experience, gained from practicing on the mat. Language directed toward the practicing practitioner contains mostly words of instruction or direction. This includes emphasis on the regulation of self to some degree, as well as the mental and physical watchfulness necessary in order to stay present and active in each posture.

In Trauma Cooperative Yoga® the teacher conducts the class environment to be one of consensus. There lacks a presence of all-knowing, yet an emphasis on the empowering choice of sharing remains intact. Rather than demonstrating what the facilitator knows, with the intention of therefore seeing the practitioners who are in the room follow along to the best of their ability, the facilitator feels into what is most present in the moment, within their own body, and encourages the attending practitioners in class to do the same. The power dynamic is deconstructed where the teacher is meant to deliver the class deemed best for the practitioners to practice on that given day. Instead, the language of honesty is brought to the forefront and in this spoken agreement to be transparent the onus is no longer on the teacher-practitioner to demonstrate postures as they should be, as according to age old master yoga teachers, but as they actually are given the restraints and liberties held within the body on that particular day..

BREAKING BEYOND SELF-CONSCIOUSNESS

As described above, TCY® teachers are asked to forego the demonstration of a pre-planned class that they have perhaps written out beforehand but to instead practice the art of presence by shifting the demonstration to be one of a yoga posture to one of inner connection that then leads to the detailed description of safe exploration of whatever physicality is involved. There is resistance that comes up for facilitators as the attention shifts from instructing a posture to sharing the process behind the decision to practice the posture in the first place. One being that the facilitator comes up against feeling as if they are taking up too much space, or too much voice is being given to their own experience.

On the contrary, the very commitment to indulging in one's own experience further creates a bond and sense of safety and security for those attending the class. This is because those very people are then encouraged to do the same. When the facilitator meets the inward self without emphasis on knowing what they are to encounter in that moment, based on a script that they've preplanned for the class, an awakening occurs unlike any other. The practitioners in the room who have shown up to practice under or with your guidance sense the lack of preconceived notions, and they themselves desire to know more of what is within them. Being an effective facilitator requires the willingness to disrobe oneself from how one wants to be viewed and summons the self that the world beyond the yoga mat yearns to witness. Whereas people often go to television to experience an unfiltered, unrestricted, life that is lived in full abandon deep down inside there is a desire to be equally as free. If not for the duration of their days, then at least for a number of collective hours that they can remember long term. The most inward part of self wants to create memories that can be called upon in the most mundane, cyclical, or even challenging moments. The yoga mat is in general a place of freedom. But, freedom means different things to different people. Freedom enters and is delivered to people in different ways. Freedom feels different to people and wakes people up in particular ways that don't always point in the same direction as the neighbor's sense of freedom. Yoga as a craft and skill, as designed by facilitators, warrants the utmost respect for its ability to enliven the practitioner. Yet, if active choice is not a part of that awakening, to one's own presence and consciousness, then the total product utilizable by that practitioner, off of the mat, is made less translatable. If the yoga practitioner and facilitator truly believes that yoga increases the well-being of its enthusiasts, and devotees, then we as conscious living, breathing, beings *must* continue to evolve and consider the further implications of such claims.

It's not enough to tell people that they're going to change because they practice yoga. And, it's too much to tell people that they have a shot at being like you, as flexible and strong, centered, and grounded, as a warrior, if they keep showing up... Both are egregious in their own way in the face of truly and effectively being an anchor of change for the seeker in your presence. As facilitators we recognize that people arrive at their mats for all different reasons. One might be because of a void in sense-of-self; the world has become so loud that they can no longer hear the echoes of truth within. Another might be that they are trying to perfect themselves. Therefore, the more we show a glossy or highest version of ourselves the more we build into a false narrative that perpetuates the distancing from true-authentic self.

We have taken time to reflect on why people show up, as well as some of the fears that might be present as to why speaking from an "I" place, in simple speak, might feel overly indulgent and cause self-consciousness. But, we've only just touched the surface on the structure of a TCY® class. This work of leaning into the role of facilitator, and shifting out of the role of being a deified instructor is vast. It's the inner warrior's work that allows oneself to rise to the kind of excellence that increases the chances of bringing out other people's inner warriors founded on inward truth versus external competition. Or, promised ideas of being able to touch your toes further than you did yesterday. The most experienced practitioner knows that those outward accomplishments come in time. Most noteworthy though is that they arise from an inner stilling that can only be reached when one is calm enough and self-referential. All the straining and tensions arise because of a false narrative around one's expectations of self actually being real in the first place. The gradual meeting of self is what brings the greatest reward.

STARTING WITH THE SELF

As beloved yoga teacher, Seane Corn says, "To truly understand what it is to be in the light, you have to also understand what it is to be in the shadow. Because it is one thing to hold the light within myself, but how can I hold the space for another being when they are in their shadow and still love them? And not judge them? I am only going to judge them if I am still judging me." These are simple words that transmit a fire to the listener or reader. Trainees who are in the process of becoming a TCY® facilitator may run the risk of losing track of the way of being that strategically deconstructs the constant extension of self in the classroom as a byproduct of what they have learned and instead steps forward with how they have and are coming to learn it.

The key with shifting into becoming a TCY® facilitator is to allow the fear of taking up space to subside and to realize the gift of transparency in its place. There are of course two ways of managing this genuine sharing of authentic self. For example, if one is talking about how the tension in their hip surfaced last week when they were bicycling then this is far from being of the essence. However, if one is saying, "I am noticing restrictions in my hip at this moment. So, I am choosing to practice the posture like so. However, here are a couple of other ways that might work for you." then in a very basic way, like this example, there is less of an onus for people to extend their empathy beyond their own mat. When we overshare as teachers it's not vulnerability or strength of transparency it's self-consumed and obnoxious.

Facilitators start with the self as a divine act of humanism. Just as part of the humanistic life approach in a psychological sense is to take responsibility for self, facilitators with an integrated TCY® approach are asked to deem their own yogic journey as one worthy of being seen, and known, in as neutral of a setting as is possible. In the other direction, of discluding the self and mention of it, facilitators short circuit their own rite of passage to knowing an inclusive self. Whereas instructors are often asked to put their best foot forward, and show postures by the book, in their tradition, or else therefore lose perceptual touch with the very roots of yoga itself, in TCY® the postures almost take a back seat in their all-importance. Instead, emerges the fully rounded self, that positions the construct of the postures themselves, and gears the self for greater knowing of the why behind their actions. This work, as Seane Corn says, starts on the mat and is meant to move beyond it. How do we get people to claim their space as their own?

KNOWING OF THE SELF

As the body opens, the brain registers the movement as new beginnings. Information is stored and brought back to life with the next time the practitioner takes the risk to examine what is within, again. Although human beings are wired for desiring acceptance and praise it often comes at the risk of knowing oneself. Ironically, our impetus for this outward acceptance is to have a sense of control in our own lives. This comes at a price. For this outward acceptance is labored through self-deceiving notions. Yoga is meant to unite the parts of self so that they whole may emerge. The whole is mighty enough to combat false narratives of self. The same narratives that seek perfection and adulation.

The yoga mat must be a refuge from the false narratives of self and the teacher-facilitator must advocate for the bringing forward of the new self, as the practitioner chooses for oneself to be, in order to then freshly re-enter the world. In order to succeed at this, bringing out and re-entering the traumatized self must know it's safe. Whereas many families and communities have created external reward systems that support the thriving of citizens of the world, the yoga mat is a place of sanctuary that must emit solitude within oneself. Where decisions are being made based on internal happenstance instead of external demand. The trauma survivor is proficient at denying their own internal experience in order to either save themselves from the confrontation of an avoided truth or to spare those around them from having to endure what they've gone through. Or, in some instances, both of these dynamics remain true for the survivor.

We cannot illuminate the road to self-recovery, *nor save people,* through externally guided systems, as the "healer", or in this case, the facilitator, can only be present for so many hours of the day for the practicing practitioner. We can unburden people from believing they are the only ones who encounter such hardship by leading from our own contact with self. It is only as navigators of present material that we open ourselves to the possibility of palpable change. The yoga mat is a place of direct contact with self. It is a place for active truth to exercise itself. This can only be made possible when there is room enough for the journeying self to emerge. Otherwise, the destination remains locked inwardly without a key.

CONCLUSION

As the famous artist, Lauren Bacall, said, *"Legends are all to do with the past and nothing to do with the present."* In other words, no matter how much we adore our yoga teachers, for the places we've gone because of their teachings, at the end of the day, we are all in this together. We are all blazing a trail, as independent and interconnected seekers, and are doing our best to show up in our fullness. So, too, we as teachers and facilitators, are meant to awaken this same freedom in the people before us, through the narration of choice, and the inwardly meeting of novel truth. In Trauma Cooperative Yoga® the facilitator is asked to put aside their own desire to be great, or to emulate a highly-realized, overly-deified, yoga master. The facilitator is instead asked to embrace the moment to moment self-findings, with the intent to relate to the present experience. And, in so doing, to enlighten both self, and the practitioners joining into the class to practice, based off of transient truth. We all rise. We all fall. Today's greatness replaces yesterday's greatness. As Caitlin Moran said, *"You don't need to be legendary all the time. You can just be legendary for ten minutes a day."*

Part Three |

Navigating Forward Motion

Chapter 12: Holding "Valid" Space as Teachers and Facilitators

In *Conquer Trauma Drama: Get Your Life Back*, trauma is referred to as being any life event physical, sexual, mental or emotional in nature that comes as a shock to your central nervous system and shakes your core beliefs about yourself and the world. Without a doubt, guidance and support are needed in order to move past a traumatic life experience. Do you notice how the word “any" is in there? That’s because it doesn’t matter if someone else doesn’t recognize the weight of an event that adversely impacts your life in the past, present, or future.

If you have consistent dis-regulation in your bodily functions combined with an involuntary reorganization of your mind’s thoughts and your consciousness’ core beliefs then you are likely to feel lost, overwhelmed, and uncertain of how to deal with the previously perceived normal day-to-day tasks. This said, it is key to innerstand that when this book and its coinciding online teacher training frames trauma as being big-t, or little-t trauma, it is to communicate the nature of the physical outward event that causes the survivor to have adverse effects in the aftermath. Not, to describe if it is relevant, or not, to be affected by the event(s). Nor, is the label of ‘little-t or big-t’ to determine if the survivor is right or not to have been affected by the event(s) in the first place. If anything, this reference point gives deeper roots to exploring and communicating one’s experience with other survivors or perceived outsiders. Now that we at least understand this, let’s look at examples of little-t and big-t traumatic life events. Little-t: as *Psychology Today* describes this is where your life nor your bodily integrity is compromised in any way. Events that might fit this description give or take the details of the event are:

Losing a pet. Hearing petty gossip about yourself. Losing sight of who you are. A breakup or divorce. A significant loss of money. Repetitive travel or moving which displaces one from a sense of belonging and therefore also safety, trust, and community. Going to work only to realize it has closed overnight without anyone telling you.

We will explore this more in the 200 hour Trauma Cooperative Yoga® Training at www.InnerBeatYoga.com.

On the other hand, big-t trauma is where your life and/or your sense of self were at great risk. For example: Combat. Rape. Blackmail. Being held hostage. Identify Theft. Having to enter a witness protection program. Losing a loved one to murder. Enduring a natural disaster. Experiencing a car/plane/train/motorcycle/bicycle crash firsthand or saving someone from one.

If you stick to the above definitions of what determines a big-t or little-t trauma you will be guided to understanding, and being able to relate to others, when they are experiencing one, or both, of the above. We cannot fully understand until we've walked in another's shoes. However, we are most empowered as people, teachers, and friends when we do our best to allow connection with others no matter how serious their present-day situation is. We can best do this when we are unafraid of the full range of human emotion and human experience that naturally exists in the world.

The Positive Side of Triggers

When we think of being triggered we often think of being overtaken by raw emotion or a wave or memory that is a disservice to us in the moment. It is key to realize that whereas triggers are very real for all of us in often extremely personal ways they have a counter use as well. Triggers can be anything from sounds to sights to body sensations produced from the outside-in to smells to even tastes. The special reality is though that none of these imply negative. For this book, we will call triggers anything external that produces an internal response.

Here are some examples of a few ways one stimuli, in this quick example of perfume, can appear in a trauma survivor's life: • The smell of perfume. • The physical feeling or sensation of applying perfume scent or essential oil on the inside of your wrist, or neck. Or, feeling someone else apply the perfume. • The sight of someone applying scent to them. • Tasting the unexpected environmental scent on your lips. • The sound of a glass bottle of any type breaking on the floor. It's not whether the trigger is planned or unplanned that it will either have a positive or negative impact on the survivor. It is instead how the survivor and the survivor's immediate support network interpret the trigger on a conscious and unconscious level that determines whether the survivor will have a positive or a negative temporary experience, or long-term experiential outcome.

With self-study practices, as is a cornerstone in yoga philosophy, we become more and more aware as our lives revolve around what our triggers are and as we successfully move beyond the triggers themselves. Of course, we are never perfect, and it would be unfulfilling if we were perfectly abreast at all times of how we might react to all life circumstances, and our environments. However, the effort of learning what we are impacted by and how our being impacted shows up is valuable to modify both our present and future responses. In modern day culture now everyone seems to be talking about responses versus reactions as is also explored in the 2015 book, *Conquer Trauma Drama: Get Your Life Back.*

It is no wonder why response versus reaction is hot to many of us who are looking to gain self-mastery as much as we are mastery over perfectly crafted self-images on social media. In order to create real results in our lives we need to be real with ourselves about how we are impacted by external stimuli. We only have so much energy. Whether we realize it, or not, a certain amount of our energy is bound up in preserving our authentic feelings for when it's "appropriate to feel them." By restricting our authentic feelings from arising to the surface to be acknowledged, and perhaps then deeply and inwardly felt, we stifle our ability to have more energy and insight for unraveling why we are impacted the way we are, and most importantly *what* we want to change about the current and revealed reality.

Review and Scope of Practice:

So far we have learned about triggers being an inner response to an external stimuli that in reality are all neutral based on what we make of the stimuli, on both a conscious and unconscious level, that then determines our chances at responding versus reacting. Triggers have an impact that drives personal feelings, personal thoughts, and personal actions that then impact other people in one way or another whether admitted to, or not. Triggers can sit in our mental awareness but are best to be felt in the whole self so that the feelings that accompany the original trigger, whatever the trigger is in actuality, can evolve and shift to their next and natural stage of existence. This will prompt new mental realms, too. The scariest reality for many survivors is that triggers symbolize the feeling of the unknown aka what will happen if I become triggered as well as the sense or belief that we are out of control. Whereas we as survivors can feel quite out of control when a trigger occurs as conscious self-studying beings we are 100% capable of recognizing, and through allowed experience shifting onward from, one feeling or emotion that is a natural byproduct of a trigger.

Whereas it is essential as a Trauma Cooperative Yoga® facilitator to know about triggers in a more complex way than it is for someone not facilitating a trauma aware yoga class it is not the facilitator's place to interrupt any signs that the practitioner is being triggered with direct contact or direct instruction outside of giving a general consensus statement to the whole group. Trauma Cooperative Yoga® in fact is an intentionally cultivated setting where survivors are given the space to be as they are. This may look as different as any of the following: • Blowing one's nose. • A runny nose left unchecked • Standing still, while everyone else is moving. • Walking out of the room while everyone is in final resting posture. • Writing in one's journal feverishly. • Eye contact. • No eye contact.

Instead, a whole class inclusion cue might be given in place of a direct instruction to the person of concern. It is key to realize that people are going through what they are going through because that's what they need to go through. There is nothing to fix. We are here to be of service. As Dr. Mary Shields says, "Helping is hierarchical" because in reality we all need help in one form or another on a daily basis. The context of the help needed or the degree of help needed is the only difference between people on any given day. However, to realize that we are being of service to assist survivors in greater and more profound self-exploration than survivors might otherwise find or discover on their own at home is groundbreaking enough. We must realize as teachers that we are not here to heal, fix, or help. We are here to guide, demonstrate, facilitate and share both insight and knowledge from our personal yoga practices, and professional yoga education background.

Chapter 13: How to Work Within Scope of Practice

The deeply analytical or spoken assessment of feelings when in regards to the yoga practitioners in front of you as a facilitator is beyond your scope of practice. Now, silent observation of mannerisms, and body language, acted upon without emotional bias with respectful and boundaried general consensus statements, is an entirely different category of feedback. Our objective as Trauma Cooperative Yoga® facilitators is to bring people further in touch with themselves as a free agent who can operate outside of the confines of their original trauma(s) and test new ground on the foundation of the yoga mat. Whether this means the survivors before you are learning to operate from a newly-liberated mental space in order to perceive themselves in new ways, or from an active mind-body connection where choices are being made on the spot as to how the survivor desires to move within their body, or in relationship to new sensation arising within the body, is none of our concern. However, our job is to move and speak slowly enough that people's chance of practicing a posture in a repetitive, unmindful, or harmful way is minimized.

Our job is to show through our own embodiment as facilitators that coming into deep contact with the self is a source of pride rather than shame. Our job is to be steady enough in the flow of the class so that the practitioner feels that they have the chance to respond to stimuli, and dialogue, in a way that is honoring of themselves. Our job is to consistently remind practitioners of options as well as of the opportunity for exploration within the direction initiated. Our job is to create a thoughtful environment where micro-movements feel as impactful on the mind, body, and emotional systems as possible. Our job is to educate on both the inward felt benefits as well as the outward physical benefits, as felt by the integral self that is participating in the self-exploration, alongside all practitioners, as well as those benefits that are anticipated that the human body as a whole might be coming into contact with inside the structure of the practice.

Silent observation

We are constantly noticing things about people. Now, of course, what we do not know is if this is the first time they've made a certain body movement, sound, or facial expression, or the umpteenth time, or the last time that they ever will. This unknowing alone creates the premise for reserving judgments that might impact how you may interact with the practitioners in front of you as a facilitator. In fact, it invites the grounds for a welcomed transition within the mind of the facilitator from formulating and acting on judgments onward to pausing in the welcomed unknown and securing greater connection to the people around you with the sharing of your own self-education.

General Consensus Statements

When we observe practitioners in front of us we will see many nuances about their character in that moment. We've already listed a few: how they hold their bodies; their facial expressions; the sounds they might make, and how they take up space in relation to their yoga practice neighbors. Still, our best facilitation is when we refrain from formulating a story about all these details, *pause,* and possibly gather a string of thoughts, or a single thought, in the form of a statement or question that might support the person or people in front of you to delve yet deeper into their inner observation. If you've ever taken a coaching class in your professional life then you will know that there are different kinds of statements or questions you might present as a facilitator. Some are more effective than others...

Stay Away from *Leading* Questions or Statements

These are things that you've already formulated as truth, albeit unchecked or partial, in your mind based on a conclusion to your analysis of a person. Remember, the **last** thing we want to do is conclude because we don't know the nature of the pattern, or lack thereof, that we are observing. It might be the first time, umpteenth time, or last time that we observe someone moving in the way that you witness them moving in that present moment. We also do not know the cause, if it has roots in the mind, emotional/spiritual self, or body. Therefore, the best statements and/or questions to present are ones that *do not* stem from a conclusion you've arrived at within your own mind about the practitioner.. As a TCY® facilitator you will NOT be concluding about someone else's character or nature; this is more the role of a therapist, counselor, coach or doctor.

Stick with open ended questions that require deeper searching. These are any that require more than a 'yes' or a 'no'. For example: if you notice someone in front of you who lifts one arm and plops it on the side of their head instead of fully reaching and engaging the side body then rather than saying, "If you don't want to practice the pose then feel free to go to a resting posture." Instead try this: "I am noticing my side body lengthening as I breathe into my elevated arm and side body, and stick with it. Creating space in between each of the ribs is great for cleansing of the organs.. You might try it, too, or stay where you are and practice self-soothing." This phrasing does not assume that the person doesn't want to do the pose, is 'lazy', 'just isn't trying', or 'is bored/distracted.' Listen closely to your thoughts as a leading facilitator; it is great to be aware of closed or leading questions versus ones that are open ended, and the impact they have on people around you.

Chapter 14: How to Work with the Autonomic Nervous System States

Amongst yoga teachers considering the inclusion of trauma aware yoga in their schedule there is a common fear of not knowing what to do if someone "freaks out" in class. For the simplicity of TCY® plain speak, let's use the terminology of someone having an 'amped' nervous system. The outward display of this is often intense to observe as the physical mannerisms can seem frightening. What might appear to be erratic body movements, or clenched fists, is the best way for a survivor in that moment to feel free, and free it's organism, in this case the human body, of the impending traumatic impact from the past that needs to exit the body.

Our number one goal as TCY® facilitators is to hold safe space. Therefore, we need to know what to suggest doing as a vocal request of the yoga practitioner before you. Our first inclination is to want to diffuse the situation as quickly as possible so that the other practitioners in the room have a clear, and felt, sense that they are safe in their space. For the people in the room who are observing another practitioner with the disposition of an amped nervous system, it can be scary, and knowing that you only have the yoga mat space on all four sides of you as a boundary is simply not enough of a comfort. You therefore need a strong and grounded class facilitator to calmly navigate the situation.

Here's what an amped nervous system might look like:

• Pacing around the room. • Non-stop fidgeting. • The tapping of a pen or physical object against one's body, the floor, or wall. • Eyes darting around the room. • A fast uncontrollable breathing pattern. • Excessive licking of the lips or biting the lip.

Here are some ideas of what to do as a facilitator. Each of the ideas give an effective way to channel the class participants' surge of energy and nervousness resulting from a triggered nervous system that is looking to become free of the body sensations. Each of the ideas reduce class disruption as much as possible. For starters, as a facilitator you might say the following, "If anyone is feeling like they suddenly are having a lot of energy and are finding yourself _______ (In the blank area this is where you point out what you are observing in the class participant, possibly one of the visual cues in the above list, such as pacing.) then you **might** benefit from going over to the nearest wall, and facing away from the wall so you can still see the class, begin to slide your back down the wall so your knees are bent. Stay there and breathe. I like to put my hands on my chest or belly to bring more sensation into my core but you might prefer something different."

Now, you've effectively taken the stigma away from the practitioner that either, 'there's something wrong or broken about them', or that 's/he needs to hide what's going on in order to be a practitioner in the class. *Great work!*

If someone is still appearing to have a lot of pent up energy then suggest, "From this position with your back being supported by the wall if you're still feeling a lot of energy you might want to practice gentle calf raises with your mind focused on your natural breath." If someone does not respond to the invitation to get up from the mat then you as a facilitator might choose to suggest using their eye focus to create a sense of comfort with all the energy present in the room. It might sound like this, "If you think it's best to stay right where you are and you're feeling a lot of energy in your body or mind then remember your single pointed eye focus. By focusing your eyes on one place it can help send calming messages to the central nervous system." You might also suggest gentle rocking or swaying from the seated position by drawing circles with the torso and/or circles with the arms. The connection to body and breath still allows the practitioner to occupy the room as a yoga practitioner. This offers constructive and proactive ways to channel an amped central nervous system.

How to Work with the 'Deflated' Nervous System

In a Trauma Cooperative Yoga® class, it is paramount to work with people where they are at that moment. That said, that does not mean that you as a facilitator ignore your own body's signals by forgoing the authentic expression of what's happening for you and instead start to approach the class by matching what others need while forgetting your own. Ultimately, we are wanting an equal measure of listening to self and others to occur in the TCY® classroom. Meaning, as we listen with our eyes, we first observe signs of a practitioner being diminished, or underwhelmed, and we still maintain to conduct the class with equal integrity to our own experience. Practitioners come to class to learn from you. In TCY® that includes learning from how you deal with your own stuff. By "stuff" we mean, physical afflictions, tight muscles, physical messages gone awry, or triggers. We practice courageous transparency while sharing with as little backstory as possible about how the physical, mental, or emotional ills came to be.

Possible Physical Indicators of the Deflated Nervous System:

• Shoulders rounded forward. • Little to no physical movement • Head hanging down • Downcast eyes • Slow speech • Little to no physical visibility that they're breathing aka stomach unable to be seen subtly expanding as s/he breathes

These are all things that we notice as facilitators without saying anything directly to the person, or conjuring a story as to why this is so. This guideline applies to both someone you just met, as well as a longtime attendee. This is because the physical indicators, as we are now aware of, change throughout the course of the practice and depend on someone's day. The less we become attached to stories, the quicker the practitioner can shift them. It is worthwhile mentioning that as the brainwaves of a yoga practitioner lower to below the racing beta brainwaves mode, that many of us in society are in most of the day, it is at this time that the brainwaves lower that *the subconscious mind is more apt or likely to take in those thoughts or projections of the yoga teacher.* Therefore, if you're projecting to them that "something is wrong" then instead of the practitioner being more receptive to a shift in their practice the practitioner is more likely to be thinking about the projections they feel are being made of them. As leaders, if we're desiring to lead people to their inner change point, we must be willing to speak to the best parts of the people before us.

Maximize Impact: Minimize the Backstory

In the Trauma Cooperative Yoga® context we must come from a place of authenticity, in order to be effective, we also need to be prudent in what we disclose. The idea of sharing our personal experience on any level is to enrich the learning curve for the practitioner. Nothing more, nothing less. Therefore, there are languaging styles that best accommodate this intentionally-measured disclosure as a teacher.

First, the downside of disclosing too much backstory:

Attendees feel the need to take care of you. This might lead to them taking on an overachieving personality, or approach, to their practice in order to comfort you by stepping up to be strong and lead at a time when they are best served going inward and listening to their own beating drum, and needs. • The practitioner's mind might likely start "filling in the blanks" of your story and painting a narrative of your life when they are meant to be focusing on their own, in their own practice. • The list really goes on..... So, you remember not to!

Examples of How to Language a Balanced Narrative: Don't VS Do

1. "Next, I am placing my hand on my low back because I pulled it last night at the gym." **Versus:** "As I practice this pose, I am placing my hand at my low back. The warmth of the hand might help to increase the stretch and/or the back's

receptiveness to the stretch. Otherwise, you might want to place your hand here ____ or here _____." Give options.

Do you see the difference?

One includes personal narrative, whereas the other one speaks to the universal gain of this possible hand placement bringing warmth and comfort.

2. "Let's shift onto a more relaxing posture, I know I am at least tired already from this posture because of all that I've been going through lately at home."

VS "I notice that I need to pause here in a more restful posture. You might continue to practice this one, or another one that you both know and are comfortable with, or practice self-soothing in a way that calls to you to do so, too. You have options."

In this example: practitioners don't need to think about how tired we are, or our lives off the mat. They do, however, need us to show them that it's more than OK to listen and respond with kindness to the bodies' needs.

How to Mend Memory Awareness for Optimal Practitioner Integration

As teachers we need to be aware of the basics in order to best serve the trauma-affected people in our facilitation space. Whereas we do not need to be specialists, or know-it-alls in trauma, or trauma recovery, we do need to innerstand enough about why we do what we do in addition to what we do in the Trauma Cooperative Yoga® setting. We have spoken about integration as an integral theme to providing a conscious and trauma aware yoga class for our practitioners. A key component of the trauma survivor's ability to integrate is the ability to recollect a sequence of postures versus a fragmented recollection of moments on the mat such as is common with the trauma afflicted. As TCY® facilitators we can practice simple reinforcers to guide practitioners toward their best yoga experience yet, and support full self integration.

It is best to understand that as Judith Herman, M.D. points toward in her book, *Trauma and Recovery,* survivors of trauma can lose the capacity to integrate the memory of overwhelming life events. While we take notice of this idea, it is essential to realize that this inability to remember previous life events in a cohesive manner can, and often does, overflow into the present day and present day happenings. Whereas we don't always need to remember everything in the past, we do benefit from being able to stream together the present. Therefore, we can invite ourselves and our attending practitioners to revisit the class practice as part of the closing portion of the class in a simple and effective way. **Depending on how you organize your class, you might invite practitioners before or after the final resting posture to write down what they remember doing throughout the class period.**

It is suggested that even five minutes of healthful, conscious, recollection can support the rekindling of one's innate ability to reflect and therefore rewire through revisiting each of the strengths they practiced within the class. It is key to encourage people at the time that you might suggest this class activity to focus on the desirable feelings and body sensations that they felt, and when, or if, focusing on the undesirable components of the class that they frame their experience as much as possible as a challenge rather than a horrible or unbearable experience in their practice. Secondly, as an alternative or additional step, to give a recap of what was practiced in class perhaps as you thank everyone for coming in a succinct way such as, "Thanks so much for choosing to come practice today; I am glad we got to focus on some balancing in tree and warrior 3, and lengthening our torsos as we reached upward throughout the class in various postures." This is a quick, friendly, and helpful way to reinforce what was done in the class, and keep practitioners grounded and connected to their experiences.

In yoga, we really want to comprehend as class leaders that people are doing deep and great work just by being there on the mat. The idea of connecting with our bodies can be and often is difficult, especially for trauma survivors. In Judith Herman's book she also quotes Bessel Van der Kolk about the nature of memories and it truly does direct us to deeply sense the effectiveness of yoga practice for trauma survivors. In the book Van der Kolk is quoted:

"He speculates that in states of high sympathetic nervous system arousal, the linguistic coding of memory is inactivated, and the central nervous system reverts to the sensory forms of memory that predominate in early life."

By sensory it is interpreted to mean the feelings, emotions, and body sensations that are part of memory recollection. One might be surprised when they simply recognize the implications of this. As Herman points out it is rather childlike. Without too harshly judging this type of memory, or the age period that is associated with the available type of memory for the recovering trauma survivor, we might notice the power in this observation as yoga facilitators. It is essential, upon recognizing the above dynamics, to honor the subtle shifts that might occur in your class. This said, although people might not have the language, nor the opportunity to share in language the nuances of the possibly intense emotional states, or physical sensations, as facilitators we have access to language ourselves. We must use language as a gentle guide for practitioners to interpret the happenings, whatever they are, to whatever degree, inward or outward, as prompts to continue leaning into the lives they want to lead. Given that they have come to yoga, it is more than likely that they want lives filled with internal and felt body states that encourage growth and expansion. Hence, we must be very careful with the words we use, just as we might with children.

In a nutshell, we must speak of positive emotional leanings when facilitating yoga classrooms because if someone gets into pure feeling alone, without their own conscious observation of their own thoughts, it can impact in a great and meaningfully lifelong way how this person shows up in any given moment. Remember, as a TCY® teacher, to be aware of how you motivate people to participate. It might be best to revisit the languaging portions of this book from time to time in order to further instill your intentions to become a learned facilitator of Trauma Cooperative Yoga® on an ongoing basis.

Top Hardships Facilitators are Most Likely to Encounter

It is quite often an unexpected and rewarding part of hardship that the hardship itself presents incredible beauty and that itself brings otherwise unknown levels of appreciation into our lives. When we lack something we need, whether it's a person, resource, or experience, if we then choose to work more closely to make that dynamic, or desire, a reality, we then discover that as we walk on the path the experience itself becomes the bringer of gifts. This is true in the greatest time of trauma, as well as in recovery from the said trauma. As we sit with our practice, we will inherently feel the silver lining of all the work that we put into our careers, as we do what we love best with our communities.

At the same time, there is a certain type of hardship of seeing people in great need, on a regular basis, and the natural ways that the facilitator can then become affected. By affected it is meant on all human levels of psyche and soma, mind and body. It is in these times when hardship seems to be the most prominent factor in your consciousness and awareness. If you, yourself, are a trauma survivor, perhaps on many accounts, and in many different life experiences, then you're likely to have your own stories.

For the sake of this lesson, it is important that we see the very real and dualistic nature of hardship and know it's value and place in both the survivor's and observer's experience. We can only do this if we value our own life's hardships. Then, we are more readily available to impart love through our skillset and impart skills through our love.

The most common hardships that are most noticeable in survivors are as follows:

• Difficulty staying present • Having a hard time grounding into self and self's sensations • Practicing self-acceptance and/or acceptance of capabilities, and/or limits. • Trusting people around them. • Trusting the self. • Practicing containment. • Feeling Safe/Unsafe. • Feeling Independent of or connected to others. • Taking action on behalf of the self.

In this book, we have touched on what each of these bulleted points mean. If you are participating in the live in-person training, or opting to do the 200+ hour Yoga Teacher Training online, then we will explore each of these more together. 1-on-1 coaching, and consultation, is part of the training for those interested via phone, as well as video meetings if preferred. Find more at www.JoStanding.com.

5 Markers of Homeostasis to Keep in Mind

Let's take a moment to review what the idea of homeostasis considers. According to Lumen Learning online, "Homeostasis regulates an organism's internal environment and maintains a stable, constant condition of properties like temperature and pH. An effector is any organ or tissue that receives information from the integrating center and acts to bring about the changes needed to maintain homeostasis. This isn't a science lesson, rather cornerstones to keep in mind when observing your practitioners, and possibly cluing into where the practitioner might be on that day, in their self-recovery, and/or self-healing, process through the help of their yoga practice.

As we're intermittently observing these markers of homeostasis in self, or in another, we make it a mission to casually observe without staring or over-assessing. We know we are upholding the cornerstones of homeostasis at the heart of yoga when we ourselves are able to help put our practitioners at ease in our presence. We do this through combining skill and personability. As we encourage people to self regulate we ourselves are further ingraining these tendencies within ourselves. The ultimate blessing of a yoga facilitator is that you get to connect, share and grow as well within an environment that you've crafted, with shared self-healing in mind, through the practice of combined self-awareness.

Here are 5 homeostasis markers to take stock of for now in your classes:

1. Body Temperature - Does someone appear excessively cold or, on the contrary, warm although everyone else in the room is saying they're comfortable? This warrants awareness that

their body-brain-mind system is processing a lot, whether it be on a physiological level, purely physical, or mental/emotional level. All of these components of self are linked into one another. Although one might be more aware of one of these areas of self needing to process extra, the whole self is a vital contributing factor to all the elements. We must be compassionate.

2. Heart Health: Is someone complaining about their heart rate being too fast? Or, can you see their pulse in their throat or inner wrist jumping rapidly? If so, as always, be aware that they are experiencing something and perhaps offer to the class in general a slow breath pattern to practice to support the individual to return to homeostasis, and drop out of 'threat mode.'
3. Breathing: Are you observing someone breathing through their mouth really quick, or only their chest moving and not their belly at all, when they breathe? This is an indicator that they're stressed, and that's okay. Post Traumatic Stress shows up in all ways. It's key to support the survivor in your class in self-regulating by offering up one or more ways, in a casual, optional, and non-intrusive way to connect to their "low" or sensing brain selves, as they are reminded to sense the current day, and present moment, safety of the room and environment. Again, all of these are suggestions, and we free ourselves of wanting to control how other people feel, or modifying how one chooses to respond to suggestions made.
4. Eye Movement: Are you observing someone having difficulty with focusing their eyes on their chosen focal point? This might mean they are feeling charged up, ungrounded, nervous, or fearful either on a conscious or unconscious level. Encourage practitioners to focus on one chosen spot.
5. Bodily Constriction: If you are observing someone's unwillingness to practice the expanding, or lengthening, poses because they are opting to stay rounded, or otherwise, in their chosen posture, it might be best to show them with your own body how great it feels to, for example, open the

fingers, and stretch out the hands, instead of balling them up in fists. Things like this help to encourage that the body is freed up of old stress held by past hardships, or current life fears, or dread. It is essential to reinforce that their time on the mat is a chance to practice doing life in different ways, even just for a few seconds, or breaths. It helps to both wear down resistance from old, engrained, or under-serving habits, and increase the practitioner's ability to return to a state of internal ease, or homeostasis.

It is non-essential to know this about all of your practitioners at all times. It is simply something to add to your repertoire of awareness building skills. When we deliver new learning as an invitation to learn more *versus do more* we often excel at imparting knowledge. Please be conscious not to put too much undue pressure on yourself to master or multitask all of these ideas into your classes that you're learning about in the entirety of this book.

Work on integrating each lesson for at least a week at minimum if not for as long as 21-30 days before bringing your classes to the next volume of your expertise. It is certain that you will take the very best of these lessons, and continue to build onto them yourself, and possibly even adapt them to best suit your community. You will find your "go to" words that best fit with you and your offerings. Remember to keep in touch with your support system of friends, co-trainers, support circle(s), and with the lead trainer of the TCY® training program with any of your questions, concerns, and general thoughts as you move forward.

Chapter 15: The Specifics of Trauma Cooperative Yoga®

Traditional yoga, as it was brought to and shared with the United States, arrived to the world in the late 1800's. Specifically, yoga began to make strides in popularity, and its general accessibility for the public, in the year of 1893 due to Swami Vivekananda's bold move to speak to the advantages of a yogic lifestyle with the World Parliament of Religions in the city of Chicago. Whereas yoga was created by men for men only in India, it only became available to all genders when Indra Devi used her worldly power to get the decision pushed through for her to be the first female to partake in teacher training alongside Jois and Iyengar. With this Western start of yoga came a deeply reverent re-creation of yoga by Devi as she brought yoga to the United States in 1947, followed by Iyengar's arrival to the U.S. nearly ten years later in 1956. Her style honored the lifestyle of Americans.

Whereas the first inclusion of women in the male-dominated practice in 1937 was a monumental and necessary step, as the women yogis took on the positive personal power that the practice of yoga provides, the practice in other ways still conformed to the limiting traditional aspects of yoga as described in this book. Although yoga serves to recharge the spirit, mind, and body when shared with populations that are more trauma prone or who suffer from complex post traumatic stress this transmission of knowledge can bring unwanted neurosis and exacerbation of post traumatic stress symptoms, if shared without thoughtful calculation, or if lacking the use of careful language in its delivery.

The Core Principles of TCY®

In a big picture view, Trauma Cooperative Yoga® principles are simple and justly recovered from formative years of preliminary growth from infant to child to adult. The principles are designed in the right of facilitating an experience where one relearns to desire prolonged inner sense of wellness and to reduce windows of disconnect while harnessing the ability to increase the overall sense of capability and self-recovery from minute to minute, day to day. Recovery of self is especially difficult for those people who have yet to experience a fully healthy upbringing and the subsequent relationships that are produced from healthy starts in life, such as childhood. Trauma Cooperative Yoga® is founded on the widely popular knowledge that the human brain is wired to continuously grow, expand, and evolve. Whereas in former years scientists and doctors believed that the human brain stops growing at a certain age and is bound to begin to decrease in its abilities, we now begin to access what inborn earthly mechanisms, such as deepened levels of self-care, and magnified love for life, self, and others does to one's sense of self. How impossible, or possible, is it to shift from the state of mind doctors officially coined in writing in 1980 as Post Traumatic Stress 'Disorder' to the more recently acknowledged state of mind as Post Traumatic Growth? As well as, in doing so, how then likely is it that a survivor of trauma, or multiple big-T traumas can know life anew, and realize new experiences both on and off of the yoga mat?

Deep Dive into "M.A.T."

The yoga mat is a place of self-analysis and offers the beginning of many self-realizations, and self-contact, that is otherwise largely unknown to humankind. The action of laying out a yoga mat first and foremost designates a space that is one that belongs to the practitioner, and the practitioner only, for the duration of the practice. In a yoga classroom it is largely unheard of to breach the boundary of the confines of the mat's edges in order to engage with a practitioner. Meaning, a teacher is highly unlikely to traverse the boundary, and enter the boundaried space of the yoga mat when it is being used by another practitioner. It is rarely thought too much of as a 'rule', or 'luxury', to have this personal space respected as it is largely an unspoken yogic right. Yet, rarely do we hear of or acknowledge this personal space as being one that belongs to the practitioner all the while encouraging practitioners to deeply claim the space as their own.

'M' Stands for Meeting Needs:

Yoga meets many unspoken needs without too much acknowledgment, analysis, or conversation about which needs are being met. For instance, yoga allows the practitioner to be seen both as they are at present, as well as possibly in a new light. Yoga allows for a time for reflection, and increases the ability for the practitioner to center themself in a way that the often busy world simply does not allow. Yoga offers a time for regeneration of one's mental processes and personal reserves of will. The practice of Yoga allows one to assess where oneself is at any given moment. Yoga encourages the self to become empty, both of bodily tensions, and of stagnated presence of mind, that may therefore if left unchecked withdraw oneself from the inherent strengths otherwise available to them.

The following is a reflection of needs that exist within the self whether one is on the mat, or off of the mat. Yoga is said to bring union between the seemingly divided parts of self, known as the body, mind, the brain itself, as well as the emotional and spiritual selves. If this is true, then it is most of service to the practitioner, both the practitioner that exists within oneself, and the one within other people who are on the yogic path, to become as acquainted as possible with these cornerstones of self. The first time the author herself got onto a yoga mat she realized that yoga was in itself 'self-psychology on the mat.' The author was able to connect with her inner self in ways that had otherwise been unavailable to her the first 20 years of her life. From the back of the room, she made it her business to do as she needed to do, listen to what she needed to listen to, and follow cues in her own time in respect to her newly able to be sensed needs.

According to Michael Oden, Behavioral Specialist, and United States Marine Corps Veteran, in his work The Needs Based Method®, as presented in his book, *"When Nobody's Home"* there are what he calls *Needs Inventory* to be met in every person's life. Oden has allowed the following to be shared from his Workbook version of *When Nobody's Home*. Some of the needs are as follows: Interpersonal Social/Emotional; Physical Well-Being, Character, Celebration of Being, Sacred Energy, Autonomy, Personal Expression, Psychological, and Emotional Development. such as nurturance and comfort. Whereas each of these categories have a great deal more to share for the benefit of a cohesive delivery of the M.A.T. principles we will move forward.

Needs are often a source of shame, guilt, embarrassment, or even worse become grounds for punishment if or when expressed. In the event that this is true for a trauma survivor, it is then our duty as Trauma Cooperative Yoga® facilitators to provide an atmosphere where transparency is great enough to illuminate the normalcy of needs themselves and therefore highlight the many ways in which needs can and often are met within the boundaries of a yoga practice. If the speaking of one's needs as a facilitator conjures a sense of negative relationship to self, or others, then the facilitator themselves needs to best work on the reinterpretation of such needs. This will then give way to greater liberation, and freedom, within the trauma survivor's overall experience. This includes the experience on and off the yoga mat.

'A' Stands forActively Self-Soothing:

One of the most common experiences a trauma survivor has in their lives is to deny their own inner experience based on general fear, or an aversion to paying attention inwardly to begin with in the first place. Denial of what is happening inside of the self is common. In a traditional yoga practice as one is asked to most directly emulate what the instructor is doing, these tendencies to therefore disconnect from one's own experience is commonly exacerbated. It is the duty of a Trauma Cooperative Yoga® facilitator to proactively assess this risk of disembodiment often disguised as a diligent practitioner.

The function of yoga is to introduce oneself to their own making. A question that is often answered within is, "How may I meet myself on the most honest terms, and respect what I see in order to create a sense of union, or "yolking"? as the word Yoga directly translates. Unfortunately, the ability for one to pay close attention to their own limitations is often lost when one feels the responsibility to be the best practitioner, in an outward sense, that they can be in the classroom. Whereas, we as facilitators, want the very best for the practitioners studying under our teaching, and as a result of this, we intrinsically want the practitioners in our classroom to continue to excel, and challenge themselves, we need to make sure that these strides are not done at the expense of a long term gain such as true self-patience, and self-understanding.

In the Trauma Cooperative Yoga® practice we seek to guide practitioners to self-soothe under the circumstances of any prolonged sense of intensity that consequently results in the survivor fleeing from their full experience. In this, we must honor the very roots of yoga itself. If yoga is to yolk all the parts of self as one then this includes the honoring of one's emotional existence and the caring for one's own innate spirit as well. The survivors all too often think they do not have the ability to affect themselves, their inner state of experience, or their lives at large. The yoga mat, with awareness of the trials and tribulations of surviving tragic circumstances of any kind, is a place to heal the negative default patterns of fleeing, or outright disconnecting, from one's sense of the present moment.

Let's not be mistaken, that we as Trauma Cooperative Yoga® facilitators are not trying to short circuit the learning curve of stillness, or staying with the experience of discomfort so as to gain greater self-control and self-mastery. For, self-control and self-mastery are gained through more means than one. As practitioners, we access these inward characteristics through more than just the physical body alone. Therefore, by self-soothing, we are not less of a yoga practitioner at that moment. For example, when the practitioner makes the executive decision to soothe levels of great physical intensity that might be affecting their mental and emotional well-being, the practitioner is practicing great levels of self-awareness. Whereas, in a traditional yoga classroom, self-soothing is often perceived as being disorderly, not sincere enough in one's efforts, or deviating from the purity of the practice that traditionally says, "If one is uncomfortable, simply return to mountain or downward facing dog." In Trauma Cooperative Yoga® there is the option to come in greater contact with that which is arising. This includes the mental, emotional, physical, and spiritual realms. Or, more plainly put, parts of self.

So, What does self-soothing look like?

It is essential to reinforce that the psychological impact of creating a safe place for the survivor where all self-experiences are welcomed is tremendously life-changing in the long haul. The process of self-discovery, such as Yoga often provides all seekers of greater knowing, is largely able to be found within this practice as the practitioner continues to evolve. As practitioners, and lifelong learners, we must dedicate ourselves to emptying our cups, and opening to the possibility that the people led in a Trauma Cooperative Yoga® class can be and often are to know themselves on higher ground through this practice.

'T' stands for Taking Initiative on the Mat

As Judith Hermann writes in her groundbreaking book, *Trauma Recovery,* trauma survivors afflicted with Post Traumatic Stress symptoms often lose a sense of self-agency. The knowing of oneself, one's worth, and one's capability of initiating change, oftentimes becomes obliterated through the violent act of trauma. However, years of research show that when someone is aware that someone intended them harm the chances of developing Post Traumatic Stress symptoms are increased than when the cause of the trauma is one such as a natural disaster. Still, this leaves a large population and chance for the reactivation of symptoms. The symptoms of Post Traumatic Stress are enlarged within the self when there isn't any form of a new experience to be had for the survivor. In one's day-to-day life it is extremely likely that the survivor of trauma will do everything in their power to recreate a sense of control often at the expense of their own safety, or well-being. There are many unconscious methods that survivors use to self-sabotage their own wellbeing in light of needing to feel a haphazard sense of safety.

In comes Trauma Cooperative Yoga®, this is the chance for a survivor, within the boundaried space of their yoga mat, to exercise their ability to make choices that suit them best in the moment versus make decisions in a thwarted attempt to avoid the threat of being retriggered, or reliving the traumatic event of the past, that very much still lives within their being. In traditional yoga, very few choices are often being given to the trauma survivor in a classic yoga format. Meaning, instructors are oftentimes heard saying that if the current posture being led does not work for the practitioner then the next best thing is to go to the child's pose or downward facing dog. In Trauma Cooperative Yoga®, not only do we not use language that activates victim mentality, such as referring to the resting pose as child's pose, but we also yield to giving, *and encouraging*, as much free choice as possible.

The trauma survivor knows all too often the ingraining beliefs set upon them by repetitive order, or forced suggestion, that they do exactly as-is desired of them by the abuser. And, it is that lived experience albeit the past that continues to live on, and grow on, within the survivor due in part to environments that fail to facilitate active choice and the ability for one to ultimately change direction in the present moment. Although an instructor might have the best intentions, and even best vocal presentation of requests, backed by soothing vocal range, of the instructions of each posture to be practiced, *without the noticeable mention of choice,* the foundation of a truly rewarding class for the survivor is simply non-existent.

Yoga Gone Awry

The world has known toxic leadership in every arena and this does not leave behind the yoga studio. As much as a yogi seeks for truth, these same yoga practitioners are shown, time and time again, that truth itself is often avoided to great extent. In the whole of society this dynamic of willful assertion of one's reality, combined with connecting with what-is undeniably the reality at present, simultaneously happens on both the macrocosmic and microcosmic planes. When voices combine and are heard collectively the willful assertion of one's truth and the recurring shared experience of many people can collide. This practice of yoga is not for the faint of heart. The warrior postures are a common thread of any kind of yoga lineage practice because of the latent potential that these postures awaken. Therefore, when a teacher is given the unmatched power to decide the direction and outcome of the practitioners' personal yoga practice then power often does become thwarted and unjust.

There are legendary examples in the mainstream media support this general warning against unflinchingly taking on principles, and teaching technique, just because that's what has been handed down through the repeated tradition of yoga, by a teacher who has been deemed by the studying teacher trainee to be known as a master, or guru. One teaching legend in this category of holding great, and questionable, power is John Friend, the founder of Anusara Yoga, and former financial analyst, as covered by *The Washington Post*, *New York Magazine,* and many other media sources. Power, in and of itself, is used in ways that demonstrate both compassion and goodwill, and power is also translated as carrying qualities of abuse, and controversy. Power itself is not the underlying cause of misconduct in the yoga classroom.

It is the power that yoga trainees intrinsically are set up to give to their teachers, and their teachers' organizations, that can become an issue of both a professional, and personal freedom. The governing bodies of yoga influence inadvertently allow such a void of healthy power interpretation to be unknowingly present. Every teacher training school, in the vast culture of yoga, is best to have a preset body of rules, and regulations, as integrated in a necessary and mandated class addition, to the pre-approved curriculum, with the intent to further instill general safety, and personal belonging within the trauma survivor.

The uncomfortable conversations need to take place. When The New Yorker Magazine quotes Bikram Choudhury, a "hot yoga" founder, saying things like, *"If [practitioners] say to me, 'Boss, you must fuck me or I will kill myself,' then I do it. Think if I don't! The karma!"*

Then we as readers, practitioners, and yoga philosophers of varying depths, are asked to separate humor with conscious reckoning of what we actually want to manifest in our three dimensional, living, breathing, interacting, worlds. Is the place for sexual humor best applied in one's activities outside of the yoga training classroom? Or, is humor of this nature okay for the yoga community? Many practitioners come to yoga to be liberated from the constraints of a premade world, often dictated by external ideas and measures of success, reward, and even "okayness." In the yoga classroom people are oftentimes brought inwardly to their own arrival of truth and connection that is otherwise impossible to be found in the material world.

In the event that a practitioner is of adult age then said adult places their safety at their own exertion of will, and their power of interest, in order to choose the classroom environment that they want to be learning from within. This said, the proposed adult-aged practitioner operates from a place of blind trust in the educator's integrity to deliver lessons as described at the time of committing to the training. Whereas sexuality is an honorable and integral part of the whole self, to what extent is it acceptable as a teacher-facilitator to bring the sexual self into direct, body-to-body, relations with practitioners? How much does consent or lack thereof play into the gauged level of acceptability? And, even when the forcible direct body-to-body contact is non-sexual in nature, how does applying one's force to another person's body, in order to attain a superficial, and temporary, state of heightened flexibility, actually benefit the practitioner or teacher-in-training?

The sense of urgency to craft a revitalized approach to yoga itself has set upon the yoga community in the here and now. The following illustrations of this assertion are equally, if not more, abrasive than the former above mention of the hot yoga founder's misspeak on the topic of karma. The following are included in order to show extreme neglect in the past to the joining of the blissful feelings that are often experienced by the practitioner on the yoga mat, with the heightened intellect needed, in order to therefore form an inclusive, and empowering, experience for every yoga practitioner moving forward. In a New York Magazine article, *Yogi John Friend's Karmic Crash,* Friend reflects on the teachings transferred to him. In so many words, Friend speaks of how Iyengar 'created isolation between the mind and body.' And says, *"The teacher would hit us, physically."*

Tough love, or aggressive teaching tactics, are favored by some. It can look like the teacher standing on the practitioner, or physically pushing them down without invitation from the practitioner to attain 'the perfect' look. Or, as Friend illustrated, even hitting. How is it that one is capable of separating one's treatment received with the treatment they wish to give and share? Unless a yoga practitioner studies in India, this extreme level of intensity in the classroom is less popular. However, complaints written of Friend, and more so of Bikram, and Pattabhi Jois known as the founder of Ashtanga, demonstrate that insidious forms of direct and indirect contact are quite alive and well on North American soil, too. In a *New Yorker* article, Pattabhi Jois was quoted as allegedly having rubbed his genitals against practitioners' pelvis while positioned in backbends, and having inserted fingers into practitioner's vaginas to supposedly test if they were engaging their bandhas and chakras correctly. The question becomes clear, if one cannot be safe in a yoga classroom then where can one be safe in the pursuit of the practice of shared wellness? What needs to happen in order for people to be able to practice together safely and respectfully?

Becoming a TCY® Teacher

In Michelle Obama's memoir, *Becoming,* she says, "There's power in allowing yourself to be known and heard, in owning your unique story, in using your authentic voice. And there's grace in being willing to know and hear others. This, for me, is how we become." In a nutshell, this is a great sentiment to return to when navigating the basis for becoming a Trauma Cooperative Yoga® Teacher. Knowing the self from the inside out is a feat largely unmet by many aspirants of success. The process of becoming a success in and of itself is something so subjective that it requires one to hone in on what their innermost experience is in order to act in accordance to the discoveries found through the search. Being a TCY® Teacher is not for the faint of heart. It is for those possessing the mind to learn what it means to show up for oneself and the practitioners in front of them in totality rather than as a byproduct of external findings centered in proposed assertions. Therefore, take this journey with the lightness of heart that what you have is enough, and what is enough is what you have within.

Mental Dispositions

The four mental dispositions that are needed in order to spearhead one's independent work as a Trauma Cooperative Yoga® teacher *as one reckons with the process of becoming trauma cooperative* are represented in the following easy-to-remember acronym, OTIS. The four are as follows:

(1) Observant; (2) Transparency in Being ; (3) Improvisational; (4) Security in Self

In the practice of being highly observant the TCY® facilitator in training is asked to go beyond the observation of whether or not the practitioner before them is in correct or incorrect anatomical alignment according to traditional methods. The curiosity that is fueling observation in the first place is turned up a notch to expand beyond levels of mere physicality alone. As a TCY® facilitator we begin to look at how the practitioner enters the posture and how they stay within it. What does it take for the gently observed practitioner to stay within the posture? Does the answer tighten facial muscles and jaws? Is it a broken breath? Is it a dazed look in the eyes?

Sometimes although we may not be able to tell what someone is feeling if we observe what we feel as we focus on another person's being we are given felt insights into that person's experience. Studies do show that feelings and states of being in so many words are contagious. A consortium of knowledge seekers ranging from Psychology Today to Forbes, Oprah, and Universities around the world have written about emotional contagion in recent years. An article in Forbes suggests that when so-called negative emotion is experienced one ought to steer clear of other human contact so as not to muddy the minds of other people. Or, wait, until the state of mind has been shifted. However, what if there is a place where all emotional visitors are honored as valuable teachers in and of themselves? What if this place is the Trauma Cooperative Yoga® classroom?

As a facilitator the more we open our minds, hearts, and practice spaces to the crux of what someone is feeling, the less we center ourselves on exceptionalism, the more we grant higher ground for people to inwardly morph to become in alignment with healthy states. The facilitator therefore needs to take time to, "Be responsible for the energy you bring into the room." as Oprah is often known to say as the intangible mind of being is in fact perceptible to others. In a *Healthline* publication entitled, *"Emotional Contagion: Why Emotions are Contagious"* mirror neurons are pointed to for the causation of the phenomenon of contagion. It is a mentionable part of the article that *'the mirror neuron system extends beyond physical actions.'*

But, why does this matter in the big picture? The basis of high tolerance and acceptance for other people's disposition is best matched with the awareness that emotions are fluid. Therefore, to remain fixated on any one emotion as being a negative is a disservice to the practitioners before you as a facilitator. As Dr. Peter Levine highlights in his book and audio, *Voice,* to move beyond the state of fixity is one of the primary aims of healing trauma in the body's systems.

It is therefore worth considering the following metaphor that we cannot enter the great sea unless we first become the grain of sand. In a philosophical way, as TCY® facilitators we need to effectively claim our way of being, no matter what it might be coined as being by anyone else on the periphery even if they are incredibly learned folk, in order to move beyond the inherent limitations that co-exist within any one way of being. As a yoga practitioner whether practicing solo or in a room full of people, in posture, or in the mental practices of the yoga life, we cannot genuinely evolve to a greater, more expansive, experience of being unless we are to wholeheartedly embody ourselves as we are as either a grain of sand or a sandcastle in all its grandeur moving onto the next best self-realization.

The more facilitators learn to acknowledge, observe, and tolerate the full range of feelings and emotions that one experiences within them the more accessible the process becomes to transition through the perceived to be negative ones. This is an inner resolution that as described has universal implications in service to the communities that surround the inward practitioner of emotional metamorphosis.

Transparency in Being

In many traditional settings, the facilitator has been schooled to instruct or guide people through a practice that is previously prescribed to be best for the practitioners before them in the present moment. The facilitator therefore more times than not disconnects or disowns their own inner needs in that moment to be a vessel that delivers the knowledge of the ancient greats. In addition, facilitators will also guide from what they've learned in their own practice so as to bring the quality of original thought to their sharing of their own learnings from their own practice. Instead, how is it possible to unearth the richness of the present moment, and its findings, and succinctly share what is in the here and now, for the teacher-practitioner? The TCY® facilitator's goal is to equally enliven the practitioner's own sense of urgency and agency to be in the present moment.

In many yoga teacher trainings the trainees are asked to plan out classes before the class begins as a way to think about how yoga flows work in the big picture. However, oftentimes this inclination to create class flows before the actual class begins can act as a barricade to genuine and authentic present moment living. Instructors or teachers then begin to rely on logic more than their own witnessing of the present moment. That's an issue of safety in and of itself. If we cannot be heartily invested in the possibilities *of the now* as facilitators then we are merely instructing based on instructions read in a book somewhere.

If we think about each person's life, and therefore their energy flow, and unique biophysicality, then we realize that each practitioner has their own book that cannot be mimicked or reproduced in identity. Only, if we do not take time to read or pay attention to what's inside 'the book' that is before us as facilitators then we are simply running off of stale knowledge that consists of other teacher's notions based on past observations. Every person has their own inner realities. This awareness alone points to the need to cater each class to the collective spirit versus a dogmatic leaning that one class flow should fit every practitioner.

Shame on the Mat

The task here in this portion of the announcing of inner qualities is to consider what it might be like to share your own process. Instead of putting self aside to advise people on best practices, what if you the facilitator openly observe the happenings in your own body in order to ground the class efforts? This might include the sharing of the meeting of your own needs, coupled with how you self-soothe based on those needs, and following that how taking initiative is rewarding or beneficial to you. It's essential in the here and now to explore why a facilitator of any background might withdraw from such sharing. The answer leads to shame.

As Carl Jung said, "Shame is a soul eating emotion." Shame stifles our energy to be in the present moment and disallows us our genuine, honest, experience in the here and now. Shame causes a discord between what-is and what we are capable of. Instead of healthily addressing our realities with tenderness and empathy for what has become our truth we shelter into shame and seek refuge from the one thing that can change us and that one thing is the willingness to accept ourselves as we are not as our shame would have us believe we are. When Carl Jung says, "Shame is a soul eating emotion", it points to the power of the devil in shame. The soul moves us from one state to another. Or, gets us out of 'fixity' as Dr. Peter Levine calls it. So, then, how do we reclaim our souls if shame has gone to battle on it? Truth.

Practitioners of yoga don't show up to align their bodies and mind with ideas of the past nor ideas of how best to act or be. Practitioners of yoga show up on their mat to meet themselves how they are. Practitioners show up to see themselves beyond the glossy veneer of perfectly positioned truths. The journey to greatness is led by many truths. It is our responsibility as teacher-practitioners to guide people to their own inner knowing. And, this inner knowing can only be found if all that is untrue or is a soul-block can be removed.

When we as teachers show up as if we've found the best way or most advanced way to practice a posture, or flow, we illuminate not the way for people to find the same but the inner strife one feels when they realize how far they have to go. But, the real practice of yoga is not to get anywhere. It is to learn to be with oneself as if one has already been delivered to the gates of emotional and mental freedom. Yoga brings peace when practiced correctly. And, correctly has a wide interpretation once core safety and practicalities have been considered.

Therefore, when we lead with transparency we show that our path is glistening with aliveness in every stage of its embodiment. Whereas, on the other hand, if we as facilitators constantly point to the more challenging ways to practice a posture then the here and now loses its shine. Both the soul and spirit of the practitioner becomes preoccupied in an external display of knowledge. Even if this isn't admitted by most practitioners. Since we as facilitators are here to serve the vast majority of practitioners it is only fitting to consider the mental leanings of the majority. Unfortunately many people have been raised on guilt, blame, and shame. It is our chance as leaders to teach the inward path to freedom.

Improvisational

In his *Psychology Today* article Clay Drinko Ph.D.,"I know it seems counterintuitive to some that improv requires practice, but let me tell you that it really does." It might also seem like merely mentioning the need to improvise in a Trauma Cooperative Yoga® class is enough as improvising seems to have fast meaning which is to go with what is present in the moment. Yet, the skill of deep listening is what anchors one's ability to improvise. We are talking about the kind of listening mentioned in the being observant part of this written section, and the kind that exceeds visual information processing, and therefore then extends to feeling out the room, too. In the mentioned Psychology Today article, Drinko points to Mihaly Csikszentmihalyi's work titled *"Flow"* in saying, *"During flow states, individuals can lose their reflective self-consciousness."* It might be that Drinko is pointing toward the possibility of present moment living therefore increasing one's ability to improvise and the resulting freedom that occurs because of it.

Being in tune with oneself in an open and yielding sense is essential to the practice of improvising. For we cannot listen to other people if we do not first tune into ourselves. With this self-listening inherently does come freedom. But, at what cost? Is it at the practitioner's expense if you're listening to yourself just as intimately as you are to the needs of the practitioners before you as a facilitator? The answer and its impact can only be found once you as a facilitator try this proposed new approach of Trauma Cooperative Yoga® teaching.

In the book *Light on Life* B.K.S. Iyengar writes, *"Yoga allows you to find an inner peace that is not ruffled and riled by the endless stresses and struggles of life."* In order for facilitators to convey this on the mat there must firstly be an honest discussion of what's happening for the facilitator within their own being as postures are approached. Then, from this place of improvising founded on the discovery of what-is in the present moment then the moment of authentic, human to human, sharing not only has transpired but furthers for the collective well-being. Following this courageous inclusion of self-learning there is the necessary guidance, and studied intelligence, that comes forward and is graciously extended to the practitioners.

The unspoken message is, *"If I can address what is happening for me at this moment then you can, too. And, I am here for you to guide you to accommodate your disposition in this moment of truth for you, too."* In other words, *"You can find yourself in this moment, too."* There is an absence of pleasant pretending, or ignoring, or denying for that matter, of the bodily, mental, and emotional makeup of the present moment. Everything that goes down is fuel for the fire. Everything is valid. Everyone is worthy of having their truth. All the inner happenings that are brought to the surface kindle the inner intelligence of everyone in the room. Everyone is smarter and more connected to the varying human condition because of it. Therefore, everyone is guided in an experiential format, and blessed with future remembering of how they've met their challenges on the mat, when the listening is deep. Innate knowing may only be called upon where it has had grounds to be constructed.

Security in Self

Baring-all is an uneasy task. Yet, yoga teachers around the planet are asked to do just that. Show up. Show yourself as the model of what to do and what not to do. And, refer to such things in the most intimate manner possible. As in, use all the information stored within your body, and the formation of narration stored within your mind, and step forth to guide others to essentially do the same on their own mats. It is a risk to stand before people you've never met and guide them through a series despite never having any contact or study of how their individual bodies work. Sure, we have general anatomy but we don't know the strain, stresses, pressures, and adversities that those bodies have encountered and built up over time.

So, for the sake of clarity, let's explore Researcher and behavioural analyst Dagfinn Moe's contribution to Science Daily, *[It was the assumption that people] "who spend time considering what they are going to do in a given risk situation would have more highly developed neural networks in their brains than those who make quick decisions and take chances,"* It goes on to say that white matter *"that contains the brains superhighways"* is greater in mass in those who *"made quick decisions and took chances rather than those who "hesitated"* in order to *"further evaluate the situation".* The prompt here is not to throw all caution to the wind and list off instructions that seem fitting in the moment. But, to instead consider the value of imparting your own experience to then lead to encouraging practitioners to further involve themselves in doing the same. This invitation is a streamlined invitation that moves throughout the whole class by resolving to involve oneself as a facilitator in the disclosing of the details of how postures are approached, and for what causes. Mind you, the exact words, *"I invite you"* needn't be repeated incessantly in order to relay this message.

The level of sharing can be broad and nuanced. The causes are varied. In the event of emotional identification, if the facilitator were so in tune, then in a succinct and matter of fact way, the mention of a posture being approached in such a matter so as to self-soothe is ample ground for appropriate class dialogue. Additionally, if the teacher-practitioner identifies a core mental state that might detract from being fully embodied or present on the yoga mat then this also is worthy of mentioning. Involving all parts of self counts toward the full incorporation and realization of any yoga posture. Whereas people might focus general conversation around their *why* for yoga being of a physical nature the recurrence of a steady mind and a manageable emotional self are often the unspoken underlying attributes that keep people coming back time and time again.

THE ROOTS OF SECURITY

Undoubtedly, the roots of a secure self stem from the opportunity to know oneself and be fully accepted within that self. One can only be secure if feelings, thoughts, and actions are met with understanding. And, where understanding doesn't exist then at the very least *innerstanding.* Meaning, people aren't always met with words of reassurance yet there are nonverbal cues that embody sanctitude and a state of knowing. Being secure as a TCY® facilitator requires knowing your so-called weaknesses, or humanness, and being willing to share them as they arise.

In a PsychOpen research article conducted by the Department of Pure and Applied Psychology the following is stated,*"Recent research has shown that family emotional support, physiological needs satisfaction, agreeableness, openness to experience and emotional intelligence are important variables that increase psychological security*

(Taormina & Sun, 2015)." Although security is a felt sense it is also a mental process as well as an evolution of environmental factors based on accumulated human experiences. The beauty and effectiveness of bringing yoga to self and others is that beyond it being a popular word it is a combination of many psycho-social factors as well as a personal journey all at once.

It is our job as facilitators to acknowledge the inherent power that we hold. When we invite people into a room, one that is often quiet and peaceful, with its music and ambience, we are also without ever even asking for the practitioner to come into direct contact with self through the setting of intention or otherwise and therefore we conjure depth and inward connection almost on the spot. Most yoga teachers know that yoga is a practice of moving inside oneself and therefore the setting itself creates an invitation to allow all the lists and agendas to gently fall by the wayside momentarily. Within this pause from the so-called norm inward worlds are bridged.

The effect of the almost instant self-connection is unpredictable. The impact of such intimate self-connection relies on the experiences the practitioner has had throughout their lives. Whether one has had 'family emotional support' is wholly subjective and depends on how one relates to the family they've had as well as how the family itself is brought to life. This said, many people recognize family as being beyond the blood bond. Many people don't have the roots of traditional families due to dysfunctional and unhealthy nuclear family units. In reality, practitioners needn't focus on whether or not their ties are strong with their traditional family, or not. But, instead fix themself on the quality of their most relied upon and meaningful relationships to date.

Family connection whether blood or otherwise runs as deep as one's life experiences alongside the willingness of heart. Many Trauma Cooperative Yoga® families perceive their practitioners alongside them to their left and their right as kindred folk who have become their family. This is because those people even in limited instances have acted as they wish family members might've acted with words of kindness, positive vision, and compassion. Each person gets to decide the long term effects of their total life experiences. How will the relationships we have with people who have acted like family to us, or been our family, either fuel us or hinder us forward? What might we as yoga practitioners want to do about these bodily and mental impressions? How might we want to hold our bodies differently so as to communicate to our minds, hearts, and spirits that we are worthy of the emotional support our past might not have given?

As Goddard University faculty, Sarah Van Hoy alludes to the listening ear:

What will we hold?
How will we hold it?

Or, how might we on the flipside accept and honor the impact of the void of said healthy relationships, and rest enough to rebuild ourselves back up on the mat if or when the lethargy from lack of support creeps in? Oftentimes the rewiring of our felt senses takes time. And, that's okay. In fact, it's honest and life-giving to bodily acknowledge what-is in order to make way for what is to become. That's what Trauma Cooperative Yoga® allows of us.

Whereas limitations of language often run through our lives and leave us unfulfilled in our interpersonal knowing, shared experiences that go unspoken hold no definitive power over the life of the survivor. On the contrary, the felt sense that resides within one's body is as changeable as it is everlasting. In a consensual setting that fosters a reacclimation to one's self trauma survivors can feel as uplifted as in other modalities such as talk therapy. TCY® is a great opportunity to make the unvoiced "seen" and to give an actionable voice to what is seen in an inclusive way.

CONCLUSION

The trademarks of becoming a TCY® teacher are as wide and varied as they are simplistic and understated. The inner machinery that makes it possible for a survivor to flourish is called upon through the spoken and unspoken means of communication. The goal is not outward as it is to reclaim oneself and refurbish one's senses with life-giving proponents for change. Stillness, allowing, deep inner listening, spontaneity, ease, the cradling of self and the self's needs, are but a few of the occurrences from the mat. The mat is no longer a place to find oneself or elevate oneself in one's eyes or anyone else's for that matter. It's a place to know more about, hold more care for, and to further animate one's inner reality.

Chapter 16: Meditation as a Daily Practice

ALOHA

Meditation is a concentrated steadiness in being. It awards no one with a lifetime of a guaranteed sense of completion, endless life fulfillment or satisfaction, nor an elevated sense of self. However, it does give access windows to the meeting of these qualities of inner possibility. Huna.org shares the meaning of the Hawaiian word, "Aloha". Let's visit the following defined acronym and as we do pause to think about how these internal processes resonate the guiding foundation of what it means to meditate as a whole:

A, ala, watchful, alertness
L, lokahi, working with unity
O, oia'i'o, truthful honesty
H, ha'aha'a, humility
A, ahonui, patient perseverance

Watchfulness can and is interpreted in more than one way. In the trauma resolution world it can translate to hypervigilance, a state in which no detail ever goes to rest and the survivor is on constant duty. Or, it can also become a state of readiness to meet the design of the present reality in all of its surprises. There is a fine line between the difference. At the same time there is a choicefulness that coincides with the determining factor of which one the trauma survivor experiences more often than not as their underlying everyday experience.

Working with unity has many potential interpretations. If we search ourselves as yogis for what a marriage of parts of self looks like we may or may not be led to a greater sense of unity. Let's lean toward the experience of arriving at a sense of inward unity where compare and contrast, and rival and resist, are non-elements in the self's persona. If this harmony, peace, and inward shelter become a reality then the reasoning can only be because one has found a way to meditate, *or be with breath,* in a concentrated and steady way through this bringing of spirit into the present moment. Meditation is an embodiment of the practice of single pointed focus as yoga has schooled for years. It therefore has many faces, shapes, and pastimes to call upon in order to support the practitioner to meet its often exalted state of oneness. In other words, sitting still is one way but not the way.

O, oia'ï'o, is for truthful honesty. Honesty has a lingering effect. Like it, or not. What lingers remains able to be heard, seen, and felt. Meditation is therefore strictly for the fierce-of-heart. The meditator needn't be advanced in any other way either spiritually, mentally, or even physically when using multiple props to aid the upright seated position. If progress is going to be made in one's commitment to a daily meditation practice the heart center must be a portal of space for the meditator, and the meditator must be willing to enter into the heart space itself in order to feed the meditation practice. The restrictively fearful heart on the other hand is the binding keeper of the yogi who strives for a deeper, and more soulful, self-connection.

Whereas we may be scared of the truth, fear itself is a non-issue. It pushes and pulls on us in it's own unique ways yet the awareness of fear's movement within us will bring us closer to truth. The tracking of fear as it arises will harness a sense of self-attaining mastery. Running from fear drives us apart from the essence of our truth. Honesty is only able to be met if we are able to meditate with a quality of okayness with fear as it arises.

Humility has many working ways. It ignites a sense of self-expansion. Although that might sound counterintuitive, humility is a supercharger of ability. As we practice humility in our lives we can converge modesty and heroism. When we know within ourselves that no matter how great our path has been or is great both to ourselves and our peers there's always more height to reach. If we know that the horizon expands for senseless miles of incalculable measure and if we are willing to be steadfast and root not in a promised direction but in ourselves then we become our own heros.

"Ahonui", or patient perseverance, is when the eye meets the storm. In meditation we must be willing to know both the fear and the failure that are possible in that we might not meet the definition of our own or someone else's expectations of their meditation practice. Yet, hold fast to the mental knowing that we will meet within ourselves what we are meant to within our own time. As meditators we allow the eager anticipation that we might store in our everyday lives to slide away from our inner experience, for the betterment of our learning, in order to become our next realized state. We patiently allow ourselves to surface beyond the titles, roles, parts, and attributes of success and failure. We learn to pursue the unknowing of our paths with the perseverance to enter the start of the trail yet begin with malleability and yielding to new encounters.

The senses of a meditator expand and grow manifold as personal identification shifts from known forms to an infinite space of possibility. The meditator's mind is capable of great things. However, expectations such as the ones we have for our lives in action are best to be placed outside of the forefront of our mental pursuits and instead become a facet of our general awareness. At the earlier stage of each sitting of each meditation it is best to be uninterested in mental, emotional, and spiritual pursuits of all kinds. The mind must be even versus biased toward one outcome or another. This allows what-is to first arise and be seen and honored. Only then does the newfound cavernous and warm, sheltered mind become a lantern for the envisioning and energizing of what-is most deeply rooted in the meditator's existence before all time. This is made possible because what is *not* the meditator has been given a chance to subside through knowing itself.

The Depth of the Practice

Just as one might gather from watching the Hawaiian way of life, the greatest passageway to a life worth living is one where we enter into our days with a sense of ease. The mental state of ease is one where the human brain waves are rolling in alpha or theta. On the flipside, when we have too many beta brain waves we become anxious and overly excited, too cautious, and even skeptical and distrusting of the flow of life. Creative acts are the fuel for feeling the benefits of ease and calm and are oftentimes made possible *because the mind is clear enough* to process a new thought pattern.

An article entitled, *'The Neuropsychological Connection Between Creativity and Meditation'* found at ResearchGate.net provides the following factual basis for the thorough examination of how meditation has a growing impact on lives around the world. "Mindfulness reflects the ability to attend to emotions, thoughts, and sensations occurring in the present moment. Mindful practices, such as meditation, are believed to enhance multiple aspects of creativity, including perceptual change, invention, fantasy, and visualization. Mindfulness and meditation may facilitate forms of problem solving that require insight and creative responses. In mindfulness participants had less "tendency to be 'blinded' by experience," in that they were less likely to perseverate in the use of old, familiar strategies. Horan (2009) concluded that mindfulness meditation supports creative thinking and cognitive flexibility, by enhancing awareness, sensitivity, and cognitive performance ."

If we are to follow the meditative path the best way to therefore do so might be to engage in a meditative practice for a few minutes a day to continue to etch away at the inner resistances to change. Although the science of meditation points toward incredible neurochemical change, the personhood within each meditator has its objections and preferences for life regardless of the long term impact being favorable or not. The desire for and pursuit of a new life and change is best to ease into for the gain of long term personal, social, ecological and even economic advantages of *moderately* doing so. EOCInstitute.org quotes the following social implications of the meditative practice, *"Researcher, neuroscientist, and pharmacologist Candance Pert, Section Chief at the National Institution of Health, found that meditation can contribute to the release of endorphins, which give you "runner's high" and just make you feel better about yourself. When we feel great about ourselves we fix the very root of social anxiety."* Whereas that statement has psychological components that might be rooted in beliefs including beliefs about the world the science within it is irrefutable. As Amit Ray says in the book, *'Om Chanting and Meditation',* "If you want to conquer the anxiety of life, live in the moment, live in the breath."

Ecologically speaking, the impact of meditation's awareness building can only be in favor of creating a more just pact and alliance with that which sustains us. When we have a reverence for life itself our connection with our roots is more deeply accessible. It's only through knowing of the body of our present day experience that we can work more deeply into the circumstances that create that experience in the first place. This includes the building of the necessary reverence for our social lives, our health, and our relationship to the whole of existence that is beyond our finite mental comprehension. The root of our lived experience always comes back to ourselves. Meditation is therefore a key part of gaining momentum in our sense of inner power. Then, we realize more worthwhile moments in the outer realms of reality.

David Attenborough, the author of the book *A Life on Our Planet* calls to the reader's attention, *"It is that range of biodiversity that we must care for - the whole thing - rather than just one or two stars."* Meanwhile, in the town of Surf City, North Carolina a sign in the name of land conservation reads, "Please stay off the dunes to conserve the beach." Whereas that is a quick way to convey the message of staying off of the sand dunes, the truth is that the sign in all honesty is best to read, "Please help protect the local houses, roadways, and businesses by staying off the dunes. They play a key role in our environment!" The beach itself is mightier than the buildings and temporary asphalt that surrounds it's giant swelling potential. People walking on the dunes put the local communities at risk. Not, the beach.

Meditation increases the meditator's ability to see cause and effect in the whole of life. Whereas many people might walk right past that well-meaning sign and nod their heads in agreement, the reality is that in order for a passerby to be able to cogitate the mind needs to be wakeful enough to perceive the difference between the two differing implications. This same wakefulness that meditators are blessed with as a byproduct of putting two and two together because the mind is quiet enough to infer the meaning of the world around them is what is required for more cause and effect relationships to develop. PubMed states,*"Meditation increases regional cerebral blood flow in the frontal and anterior cingulate regions of the brain, and increases efficiency in the brain's executive attentional network."* It's a wonder more people don't meditate on a daily basis.

Meditation is actually more simple than meditators might make it out to be. There is an element of trust in the process and allowing. Indeed, these are two intangibles that can be rather trying at times especially if or when living in a so-called logical world version of reality only. In the collaborative publication QC Voices featuring writers from Queens College an entry on the study of mathematics says, *"When reading mathematics you have to peel the words and symbols off the page, and turn them into a concept in your head."* Although one is not necessarily reading while meditating, although if one is reading with a single pointed focus in a quiet and comfortable environment reading itself is a form of meditative practice, this description by this Queens practitioner is fairly symbolic of the crux of meditation. As previously described, before any act of creation or higher realization might take place within the meditation practice the page or canvas of the mind must be clear of the meditator's prior projections. Finally, although we are not seeking to cogitate our way to new concepts as this mathematics quote suggests, the appearance of new inner knowing does surface as a result of the preliminary mental clearing.

Submerging into the New World

The *Scientific American* magazine published an article called *Why Your Brain Needs More Downtime.* In it a man's experience of being drained from work overload and then taking a respite is recognized as such, *"...Gradually, his mind seemed to sort through a backlog of unprocessed data and to empty itself of accumulated concerns."* The article surveyed these workers to discover that a commonality was revealed amongst them, *"...they were reaching a breaking point after which they would not be able to accommodate the deluge of data."* The meditative practices he participated in to soothe himself were what brought the man refuge from the pace of his work demands. Although meditation has a daunting implication of being able to transcend all the chatter in one's mind, the truth is that it is a liberating practice with or without the barrage of thought streams. As this man in *Scientific American* abstractly pointed toward whether one can hear or not hear the thoughts pushing through if one is cognizant enough to recognize them as they occur there is a certain peace and satisfaction that coincides with the inner listening.

Just as we actively listen to people in our lives as they speak, if we turn the light of consideration to do the same thing to ourselves without suggestion nor expectation of thoughts being actionable or fair or just then we surpass the limitations of linear thinking. The gift of meditation is that it allows more imaginative moments to emerge in waking life thus freeing the normally imprisoned mind and giving it a chance to unprocess the rigamarole and dogma that infuses our society. If we can gain citizenship into our own meandering imaginations, equally as we do to our means to an end rational minds, then our brains and our minds will thank us in the form of the replenishment of spirit, a calmer and more clear mind, and a deeply oxygenated and cleansed body "as stress-causing carbon dioxide exits or is shuttled out," as Yoga Journal says describes the body's purification process. Keep in mind that too much carbon dioxide in the body, "damages the tissues and organs and further impairs the oxygenation of blood and, as a result, slows oxygen delivery to the tissues." according to the National Heart, Lung, and Blood Institute. Whatever form of meditation one calls into their lives it is best to make sure that it is one that encourages a natural and easy breath to live inside of the body so as to expel said toxins.

CONCLUSION

Meditation comes in many forms and is not limited to sitting still. However, to access this form of meditation on a trial basis might be most advantageous when implementing the considerations found in this body of work. The approach to meditation, such as all things in life, is the fundamental and marked difference between gaining pleasure and a sense of accomplishment from the practice of meditation. Whereas meditation itself is far from accomplishment there is a sense of having earned the mental wherewithal to execute tasks more effectively. When one allows oneself to experience the self beyond the mental restrictions and prior understandings one is capable of breaking new ground both metaphorically and literally within their own lives. The advantages of having done so are wide ranging and not limited to the improved ecological relationships, social connection potential, and self-mastery reaches.

Chapter 17: Managing the Psyche Soma Pain Threshold in Trauma Cooperative Yoga®

Pain is a feeling, concept, and whole being experience. It challenges how the survivor lives within the moment and interacts with others. On the yoga mat it calls upon self-awareness to answer whether it is responded to, resisted, a new form of distraction, or completely ignored. The trauma survivor's life quality depends on how mental and bodily pain is interpreted and mitigated in the process of trauma resolution. In this area of study the fully embodied experience of pain is explored as well as how survivors of trauma who are willing to more deeply feel pain may in fact alter total life outcomes for the survivor on the mend.

MITIGATING THE MIND-BODY RESPONSE

Marilia Aisenstein repeats in her PubMed contribution that, "Psychoanalysis places the origin of the thought process in the body." Along similar lines, Colorado-based Dr. Perrin Elisha worked dutifully in her book, *The Conscious Body: A Psychoanalytic Exploration of the Body in Therapy* to point toward that despite the limited perception of the human mind, the body is always awake to all that is being seen, heard, spoken, and touched. In Dr. Elisha's words, "Most people in Western contemporary culture have come to think of psychological space, what we think of as consciousness, as somehow not really being located in the (actual) body."

It seems anywhere from mildly to greatly neglectful to push aside the realization that words themselves are founded on direct connection to the body. How the body was ever left out of commendable texts, mostly of Western publication, that recognized only mental processes as a solution is beyond many dedicated and learned professionals around the globe today. When we pause to think of the sayings over time that have evolved from a physical relationship to words, we might make sufficient space for the body as a relationship tool to combat maladies of the mind that plague people's ability to live full and long, healthy lives. The ongoing cyclical relationship between mind and body is one that requires constant attention and precision when choosing how to best relate to one's life, and life direction. It wasn't until the learning of yoga and the like that Westerners have begun to truly pause long enough to peer within their physiological workings in order to subtly correct them. Whereas yoga has been around for great lengths of time the concept of merging mind-effective awarenesses and mental self-engagement throughout the practice is a newer concept. Mostly, because of yoga's origin this introduction of mind relevance has been and might still be belittled as simply being "not yoga." However, in the easing of pain the whole circuitry of self must be engaged. The mind feeds the body, as the body feeds the mind on where to go next in one's evolution of daily mat practice and beyond.

The sayings differ over the years and depending on which culture one is most present within. However, they show up something like this:

"S/he is a pain in my neck/back."
"I was beside myself."
"Over my dead body."

Let's break these down and their relevance. In managing pain we must begin to do the inner work of word and felt sense association so as to break down our boundaries of self. The parts of ourselves we are unwilling to inhabit or even make visible are the parts that arise in the greatest moments of pain. Therefore, skillful navigation of all parts of self is required on the regular in order to re-identify with our physical, mental, emotional, and spiritual embodiment. The first, "S/he is a pain in my neck/back." How is the pain showing up in the region of the body noticed and what does it have to do with anyone else but the person whose body is experiencing the sensation or in some cases lack thereof? There are some studies that discuss the visibility of the light body, or soul, entering and leaving the body upon birth and death through the crown of the head. In this event, that we are existing as more than three dimensional beings with a light self as part of the human journey, then is it possible that as one says, "S/he was beside her/himself" that there is a literal meaning when one is identifying with the light self? If so, then the light self is moveable and transmittable and transferable as it travels through the physical space around us and perhaps beyond.

Many trauma survivors have spoken about out-of-body experiences, or OBE's. Meaning, upon the impact of a major physical trauma whether car crash or rape, or any other kind of deliberate violence, they recollect seeing themselves aka their physical body from beyond, or afar, or sometimes standing or floating beside themselves aka their physical body. Dr. Alan Sanderson in his writing for the 180 year old Royal College of Psychiatrists contribution says:

"Our understanding of the nature and causes of emotional disorder has advanced scarcely at all. The problems posed by people cutting themselves, abusing drugs and alcohol, suffering periods of depression or experiencing bizarre thoughts and behaviour, seem as great as ever, and we remain in almost total ignorance of the underlying causes. The biological approach, which a century ago appeared to hold out such hope for psychiatry, has run out of steam. Yet, because this remains the only scientifically 'respectable' approach, nothing new is being tried. Where should one look?" By 'biological' it is believed by the author to be referring to the ingestion of prescription drugs to modify the biological responses in hopes of mind activity being changed as a result. Sanderson goes on to say, *"I believe that consciousness is a phenomenon in its own right and is not simply the result of brain activity.* While it is true that during bodily life, consciousness is closely linked with brain activity and largely dependent upon brain function, there are many observations which support the belief that consciousness survives bodily death and that during life it may, on occasion, operate independently."

Regardless of where you stand on the proposed idea of having a light body, soul, or spirit, or the possibility of consciousness perhaps even affecting brain activity is neither here nor there. As a yoga practitioner, yoga teacher, and facilitator of yoga, it is key to realize that our juxtaposition of words and body activity or lack thereof affects our consciousness, reasoning and conscious ability to affect our lives. The yoga mat is designed as a place to go within the self. It is therefore key to integrate all parts of self. Mr. Sanderson is not saying that the mind is an alien element of self that is estranged and unworthy of union with the self when embarking on significant personal change. In fact, the mind is a key part and is a fundamental source of change when asked or encouraged to connect with the spirit of self, or that which animates us, as well as with our physical organism that is our body and last but not least our emotional selves. To teach or facilitate a class that denies any part of the human self's journey is to almost suggest the people before you alienate a part of self from self. In which case, the attainment of the essence of yoga would be cast aside. For yoga is union at its very root.

THERE IS NO MITIGATION WITHOUT ACCEPTANCE

Now that the author has advocated for full self-inclusion in the practice of both yoga on the mat as well as in the practice of life itself, let's look at the function of full self recognition with the managing of one's pain. It's worth noting that the word mitigate was first recorded in 1375 in Middle English, and held the meaning, "to soothe, calm, soften". Or, "to make it less severe." Seeing as pain is a non-negotiable in life for every living and breathing person in this life it is therefore of much use to consider how one relates to it within the self first before trying to rid oneself of it. As through the process of the careful unraveling of how the personal self relates to, and navigates pain, the pain itself begins to subside.

The highly-regarded publication, *Scientific American,* reports on the work of the twenty year chair of neurology at the University of Iowa in stating, "During the past 30 years, Antonio R. Damasio has strived to show that feelings are what arise as the brain interprets emotions, which are themselves purely physical signals of the body reacting to external stimuli." It is worth noting that yes sometimes researchers, scientists, and doctors compute the evolution of self processes in the following order: feelings followed by physical sensation. However, it is also possible that feelings first arise based on an energetic or conscious installation of awareness. Then, emotions follow. Then, physical sensations, and physical movement, become a part of the human present experience as a result of the natural feelings that conjure one to emote or express in outward emotion. The author's point of view is that sometimes it is possible to recognize that one's personal feelings are the internal process that can indeed evolve from physical sensation, physical experience, or the physical sensing of the present moment. It is then that the feelings become emotions.

Emotions are "energy in motion" as Cincinnati-based energy medicine guide and author of *"Answers for Sensitive People"*, Anne Steffen-Russo, says. What the reader needs to inquire of within oneself and one's personal experience based on their days on this earth is whether or not a willingness to perceive the self in new and perhaps fresher ways is present. One is granted a new orientation to self and one's present when one becomes curious enough to sense oneself beyond the restraints of yesterday's innerstanding. Whether the self becomes grounded and "in the know" through physical sensing or an inner feeling, hunch, or intuitive sense, first is neither here nor there in the finding of one's connection with the truth of their experience. The coming to know of oneself and of one's life in the past, present, and future, is made possible through self-analysis. The desire to be attentive to the ordering of one's experience does help manifold in one's self-recovery. Traumatic life experiences can and do often distance oneself from the parts of self that make it possible to comprehend one's life in it's full magnitude. The mental and emotional selves, spiritual and physical, are a byproduct of one's consciousness. Are we willing to depart from our safely cogitated and thought worlds in order to position oneself and one's full knowing and therefore full recovery at the forefront of priorities? Learning to cooperate with one's self in the self's entirety unleashes a whole new world of energy for the trauma survivor.

OUR INTERPRETATION OF PAIN

The Department of Veterans Affairs and The Center for Integrated Healthcare begin their coverage of The Gate Control Theory of Pain as follows, "The way in which we experience pain is very complex. All sorts of factors influence our experience, *including our thoughts and feelings.*" This is a profound statement for such a professional body to make considering yoga and other alternative treatments are only beginning to be more widely accepted across the United States nation in the VA. Nevertheless, there it is, plain and simply laid out. This particular body of work goes on to acknowledge that *the level of attention* that is demanded in any one given moment in time, *and it's direction or focus*, can alter how one perceives their physical self and their pain. The patient education handout goes on yet more to share the insight, "*In the spinal cord, you might imagine a series of gates into which messages about pain arrive from all over the body.*"

The Gate Control Theory involves recognizing that the so-called gates of the spinal cord can be more open or more closed. The more open they are, the more chance of being affected by pain in an unpleasant proportion. Factors such as lack of exercise, mental attention or lack thereof, and unbeneficial stress levels influence one to experience the negative end of the spectrum of pain. More so, in an effort to dive more deeply into the research of The Gate Control Theory, let's explore Thomas Hadjistavropoulos and Kenneth D. Craig's expansion on the aforementioned subject in their more comprehensive study evolving to the neuromatrix concept.

A quick look on Wikipedia and you can discover that, "The neuromatrix theory of pain states that the perception of painful stimuli does not result from the brain's passive registration of tissue trauma, but from its active generation of subjective experiences through a network of neurons known as the neuromatrix. The theory was proposed by Ronald Melzack in 1990." So, what does that mean? To further investigate the implications of what subjective experiences means we go to PubMed for more detail. The inclusion of the following is quite leading in one's further discovery, *"Pain is a multidimensional experience produced by characteristic "neurosignature" patterns of nerve impulses generated by a widely distributed neural network, the "body-self neuromatrix" in the brain."* As a reader we might derive from this that a part of the brain is dedicated not only to the registration of pain but to bodily perception. Or, that a 'mini version' of our body lives inside of our brain and actually takes up life there. In this translation of PubMed's quoted article, "The Indissociable Unity of Psyche and Soma," perhaps this is due cause for the body's activity having such an impactful change on how the brain functions and thus how the mood and thought patterns of a person may change course through mere physical activity or exercise.

A separate quote in the article *The Indissociable Unity of Psyche and Soma* says, "These neurosignature patterns may be triggered by sensory inputs, but they may also be generated independently of them." In other words, as a so-called pain survivor, as everyone on the earth is, if we recollect or think about painful experiences the same pains and perhaps ills transpire within the self despite there being no new external stimuli causing the felt experience of pain. Yet, the article goes on to state that there is still little to no understanding of why chronic pain occurs. In the further independent interpretation of pain and its evolution it becomes worthy to perhaps derive one's own meaning and possibilities of chronic phenomena. With the sensing of present pain despite there being a lack of present day cause for the pain it becomes curious as to how one might navigate such said pain. In the case that the yoga practitioner is compelled to do so the reorientation to the body self is key in changing up the narrative and the quality of embodiment that might be influencing one's experience to become negatively-geared to recall such pain.

The Indissociable Unity of Psyche and Soma says, "Furthermore, chronic psychological or physical stress is often associated with chronic pain, but the relationship is poorly understood." Whether or not the relationship is understood or not the cause is known as stated. Therefore, is one consistent and courageous enough to be the culprit of their own change? Is one audacious enough to pursue self-inquiry on a regular basis? Is one mindful and present enough to remember the perhaps guiding facts herein to realize at each moment that choice does indeed exist as to how one experiences the world? Is one disciplined enough to check into the psychic, spiritual, mental, physical, and emotional causes of one's dis-ease? If yes, then at least as far as many leading yoga schools of thought and researchers discover that the practice of such self-considerations might heartily impact the way one experiences life day in and day out.

United States Navy Veteran and Doctor, Timothy Avery, Psy.D., Director of Program Evaluation with Veterans Yoga Project, submitted program evaluation data that revealed the following. Please be mindful this is a community of military veterans beginning to practice yoga and their experience after having done so. "Veterans provided subjective ratings of their pain and stress before and after each yoga class. These consisted of pre and post self-assessments of current pain using a numeric rating scale and stress using the Subjective Units of Distress Scale (SUDS). Both pain and stress were assessed on a scale of 0 through 10 in which zero is no pain or stress and ten is extreme pain or stress. These scales enable the class participants, the instructor, and the clinical staff to note changes associated with each class. Over this period, pain assessments both before and after each class were reported for a total of 1909 encounters. With regards to pain, 76% of all encounters were associated with a reduction in pain." In other words, after yoga class pain was reduced.

Furthermore, the Justice Resource Institute, as spearheaded by Dr. Bessel van der Kolk, did a study with people who had been in therapy for 10 years. Each had little to no experience with yoga. What the JRI found was that after practicing yoga 1X a week for 10 weeks straight their Post Traumatic Stress symptoms reduced by 33% and after 2 months upon check-in this same group no longer had enough symptoms to be classified as still having Post Traumatic Stress. It is safe to say that there is an effective tool within the practice of yoga itself. As far as pain is regarded and its management or our mitigation of it there is no shortcut. However, the answer is routinely proven to not only be within us but a natural part of us.

Concerning neuromatrix theory as outlined in PubMed there is a new layer that points toward the 'mini-version of the body' found in the infrastructure of the brain being somewhat of an instigator of the way in which one might change upon encountering pain. *"The neuromatrix theory of pain provides a new conceptual framework. It proposes that the output patterns of the body-self neuromatrix activate perceptual, homeostatic, and behavioral programs after injury, pathology, or chronic stress."* The implications of this may or may not land as strongly for some readers; however, the notion is that if one is conscious enough to manage oneself or mitigate the experience of pain in a way that takes this into consideration then the very effects, or impacted areas of concern, such as homeostatic levels, behaviors, and mental processing or perception, are sources for solution.

On a personal level and clinical level everyone who has ever decided to work with the current bodily, mental, and emotional realities that one experiences, instead of try and perhaps bulldoze them, ignore them, or shape them to be a different way, instantaneously becomes empowered to access more levels of self-command in the present moment. For instance, if one is feeling morose or melancholy and becomes aware of the feeling or perception from a neutral, non-negatively judging place then one may draw from this observation. One may discover what might need to be done in order to meet the needs of the moment, self-soothe, and take initiative. In Trauma Cooperative Yoga® the practitioner is asked to recognize one's disposition before actively working with it in a way that serves independent well-being. No one in the room nor beyond can tell a practitioner of yoga what is necessary in that moment in order to most pleasantly and consistently feel all parts of self in such a manner that said feeling is beneficial to one's sustainability of self.

The full gamut of what a trauma survivor experiences day in and day out is innumerable in felt senses, perceptions, and affectation stemming from the original event as stored in the human body and now recognizably a part of the brain. The center of power therefore is to become self-aware and quiet enough to observe felt senses before they become full-out derogatory experiences. If one cannot voice said perceptual and sensorial grievances due to societal, local community, or personal limitations then one needs an outlet in which one may listen to one's own disturbances and respond mindfully to them without building on a negative narrative nor acting from a negative bias. The yoga mat has time and time again offered a place for self-introspection that is neither fully negative nor positive but 'just is.'

It's not that lifting the heel of your foot to your buttocks in standing thigh stretch is life changing, it's what happens *when* you lift your heel to your buttock. Concepts of actions are not the same thing as the action of taking a mental concept and bringing it to life through experience. When one knows the feeling and sensation of all parts of their body the practitioner can in turn know and realize the interconnections of self within that part of the body. Author and international publisher Louise Hay didn't sell out her books because it was founded on popular culture to do the brazen feat of inner work. It's because her books were written on personal truth and that truth cast a shade of knowing within many people that the body is an extension of the human brain, or mind. In such instances, such as the neuromatrix theory constructs, the body, mind, and brain are inextricably linked and influential over one another.

FUNCTIONS OF PAIN

In the book What the Body Commands: The Imperative Theory of Pain, the author Colin Klein says that, "Returning to balance only requires taking the right sort of actions. Your body doesn't need to tell you why. That would only get in the way." In the same sentiment on a mental scale when we lack understanding around one of life's happenings or the knowing behind why someone is acting the way that they are then the act of asking 'why' is only a further path to hell. Just as with the body, the inquiry of 'why' only aggravates the experiencer of pain and further drives a wedge between the experiencer and the bridgeway of trust. Knowing the 'what' that is happening, and then what needs to occur in order to address it is a much more succinct path to body resolution on the TCY® yoga mat. Klein gives an example of a throbbing ankle with the following words, "If I do walk on my ankle, it could make things worse, maybe permanently. Rather than leave it up to me, my body just motivates me not to walk around if I don't have to. Then I will heal. That is the function of pain." In this example, the author therefore describes pain as both a modulator of action, inaction, and a potential communicator of wellness.

We have explored what pain might be trying to tell us. Now, what might pain and the experience of it be incapable of telling us? According to the Pain Medicine publication from 2017,"Self-Reported Pain in Male and Female Iraq/Afghanistan-Era Veterans: Associations with Psychiatric Symptoms and Functioning", although reported pain levels were higher in female veterans both female and male, regardless of gender specification, experienced psychiatric and functional impacts in association with their experience of pain. It is startling to realize that no matter if one reports feeling pain or not, pain-associated psychological and functional impacts are present. It's worth suggesting that one's either conscious or unconscious ability to 'unplug' from the proposed "body-self neuromatrix" located in the brain is perhaps without long lasting benefit. In one's declaration that they "just do not feel pain", what is the grandeur if it involves disconnecting from the feeling of self? Furthermore, what is the long term benefit of mismanaging one's experience of pain through pure neglect, or shutting down one's felt connection to pain, if the implication pointed toward in this study is such that long term effects still exist?

One might argue that delving into pain, by showing up for it, as inconvenient as that might be, is surely the cause for both greater self-discovery and self-mastery. Perhaps disassociating from liveable levels of pain is not in one's best interest after all. Through the course of this topic examination we have found that a consistent yoga practice benefits both psychological and physiological factors for the dedicated practitioner. However, what is yoga exactly in the form of the Trauma Cooperative Yoga® approach? As we add in presence of mind we begin to engage the full self and therefore the potential for full and long lasting personal glory.

The human brain has a center located area called the amygdala. In a neuroscience-focused intensive Sounds True podcast series, Dr. Jill Bolte Taylor refers to the necessity of addressing one's own brain. As a listener you might deduce that one even has the ability to change the course of one's mental and therefore likely physical experience, too. At the time of noticing oneself is triggered by an emotional and/or physical pain source then one is best, as according to the doctor, to speak directly to that part of the brain. In communication with one's inner voice or actual vocalized sound one might say, "It's okay. Everything is (going to be) just fine." Now, we are made aware with the gate control theory that one's experience of pain is influenced by the level of stress one might be experiencing. In which case, by soothingly speaking to oneself while holding a visual in one's conscious mind of the location of the amygdala in the brain then the so-called siren will stop blaring. The brain will stop sending the alert signals to the rest of the brain and body and the ability for one to calm oneself is now ever present. At this moment, the experience of pain becomes very different.

This is of course not the one and only method for self-intervention. However, combined with the self-awareness and self-command this is a great and promising start to intervening in the felt experience of pain. Since each type of pain, no matter its origin, does affect other areas of the self thus potentially causing them pain it is worth mentioning. There are more brain centers that coincide with the beginnings of mitigating dis-ease that inherently leads to greater or more types of pain. A consideration of self-applied, hands on, reorientation to both the beginnings or full-fledged experience of pain is beneficial.

HANDS ON INTERVENTION

In Jonathan Lambert's work as presented in NPR entitled, *Scientists Find Brain Cells That Make Pain Hurt,* the notion that the experience of pain reveals itself in the amygdala part of the brain is reinforced yet again. This time it coincides with a fantastic study, albeit somewhat cruel-sounding to mice, that serves in illustrating the central point mentioned earlier: how we experience pain is both modifiable and therefore manageable. While keeping in mind that to totally ignore it or wish it away is a disservice in the long haul because regardless of one's felt sense of it or lack thereof the *impact* of a lived experience does show up at a later date. Perhaps, when taking a long view beyond this scientific research, the pain might be asking for the experiencer to have a reorientation to it through one's conscious present attention and conscious redirection of experience. So, that the experiencer may then have worked out aversion to it and strengthened one's ability to endure such a kind of physicality, mentality, or emotionality.

In the study a research team at Stanford University used mice as has been customary in the past in order to determine the sensing, impact, and reaction of pain levels. The amygdala was the center point of focus for neuroscientist Grégory Scherrer, one of the causes for this being that the amygdala is a regulator of emotions. As you might recall from The Gate Control Theory human emotion and the degree of pain one feels are interlinked. If one is stressed it implies having negative emotions. However, the intentional application of stress on the body such as in massage and exercise as is overseen by the self is a kind of strength-sourced stress. It is negative or toxic stress that is being referenced here that is largely ignored and thus left unattended to thereby causing a build up of this undesirable stress and its toxins in the body. In which case, such accumulation of unaddressed stressors is registered in the amygdala.

In the Stanford research the scientists sure enough found, *"a constellation of about 150 neurons in a region called the basolateral amygdala that were active only when the mice appeared to be in pain..."* As an aside, in the name of both humane research tactics and human empowerment systems, it is key to note that the mouse has consciousness *but no mind* to navigate the successful mental, bodily, and emotional *reorientation to the felt pain experience* so that it becomes one of more *neutrality* and not suffering. One may also possibly say the same of someone's abilities or lack thereof who is overly-medicated. Moving forward, in discovering the bodily reaction of the mice who have on average a confirmed 85 percent identicalness in genomes to humans, and up to 99 percent the same in identical genes, as according to the National Human Genome Research Institute, we come to potentially know more of ourselves as people. The scientists uncovered that they were able to switch the pain neurons *on and off* within the amygdala. This ultimately meant that when these pain neurons were turned off the unpleasantries and suffering associated with pain also ceased to exist. Note: the mice were still aware of pain however it no longer exhibited stress behaviors and was no longer consumed in their attention to the pain itself.

As people, let's pause and imagine the implications and revolutionary side effects of being able to reroute our felt and lived experiences to directions that instead nurture our ability to be in the present moment, and tend to the order of our lives' top priorities. Pain is a source of not only the loss of life experiences but to the ability to be with oneself, within one's own thoughts, and therefore one's own chosen reality. If you are one to feel the pain of others then it is groundbreaking if not lifesaving to learn how to best mitigate one's own experience whether it's direct or empathic with varying levels and versions of pain.

DISRUPT THE PATTERN

In processing the power of holding our attention toward the brain regions while remaining aware of the brain parts' function we become able as people to intervene *and influence* functioning of the brain. With this train of thought in mind, we become aware that this awareness then also has cross-applications to our other brain regions. Within both the physical connection and the mental-focusing connection we move our spirits to collide with the very matter that is at hand. Let's take the next moment to consider the other areas of the brain and their relevance.

THE BASIS OF ACTUALITIES

In the book, *Psyche and Soma: Physicians and Metaphysicians on the Mind-body Problem from Antiquity to Enlightenment,* it is written,

"Few subjects have stimulated a more intensive intellectual interchange among physicians and philosophers than the nature of the human soul and its relationship to the human body." This self-work is definitely soul work. It needs to be acquired within the self, from the self, and for the self before it may be passed on for the benefit of the practitioners before you in the yoga studio place. This work calls on all parts of self. In order to revolutionize one's own body and mind and the functioning of these parts in order to therefore cater to one's ultimate vision for life itself we must yearn for change. Change within the self is the utmost first place to look in order to be able to influence anyone or anything else. The answer of the self is only realized when we bring our soul presence to the mind and body work that we set out to do on the yoga mat and beyond.

We may know that we are utilizing the power of the mind and the functionality of the body together to reach the desired state of being that we envision for ourselves in any given moment. We might not know that our consciousness relies on our soul's deep desire for union of all parts of self before such a union can occur. So, before we begin this final examination of mediating pain it is crucial to at the very least read these aforementioned words, if not to feel them in the core that is you beyond all external factors. On a scientific level as published in the National Institutes of Health government website the following is stated, *"Integral physiology has to do with the synthesis of conventional physiology and how our individual psyches (i.e., mind, emotions, and spirituality) interact with the world around us, to induce positive or detrimental changes in our bodies."* Once again we are reminded of our interconnectivity between self, soma or body, and our environment. The leading question becomes what do we do about it when the impacts are detrimental in any way to us?

FOCUS

Focus on the most influential-to-behavior brain areas such as the frontal lobe, parietal lobe, and brain stem. In addition to the amygdala, these areas surface areas of self that influence how we speak, feel, think, sense, feel, and inhabit our bodies. Combine these mental focuses with choice words relevant to your situation and your desire for change. Stay mindful and present, and if it feels appropriate combine physical touch with said words and intent.

Chapter 18: Social and Ecological Justice as Applied to Trauma Cooperative Yoga®

Oftentimes, the phrase *"Get a hold of yourself"* is spoken to people when they are at their most delicate of moments. This said, in a society that overlooks the freedom or promotion of the freedoms of bodily movement on a day-to-day basis the outcome is often personal numbness, and from that numbness one's natural disposition is to become frozen in oneself. This state of being frozen is a byproduct of having the belief of non-choice so deeply ingrained that one ceases to fight, or flee, from the source of normalized oppression. The source might vary from one's lack of bodily freedom stemming from being in the kitchen or living room growing up, and asked to sit still in front of the television, and "Stop moving around so much!", or in the grade school classroom where stillness in every sense, unless otherwise stated, is revered. Ironically, getting a hold on oneself in a *tactile, self-feeling way* is *exactly what needs to transpire* in order to readdress one's life, and be in close contact with a clear and expansive self-directed life of great possibility. As one gets a hold of oneself, internal motion is then reestablished, as one is unbound by the frozen feeling, and this is followed by external limb-focused movement. Then, thankfully, any over-identification with negative judgment fades away. One might be saying *"Get a hold of yourself!"* or not and it is of non-relevance to this "life-liver's" innerscape.

The challenge comes into play for traumatic life event survivors when being in touch with oneself is so foreign that one doesn't know where to begin. Direction needs permission, and permission is a whole new blanket of comfort, or sometimes discomfort. Most people experience some level of disconnect from their bodies. However, when trauma lingers in the background of someone's life it often moves into the foreground via next levels of disconnect also known as dissociation. On a personal level, this is when life can just be lived without any reasoning, intention, common thread to the present nor the present moment's needs and considerations.

If you notice the word foreign in the above it is in fact intentional. In Poka Laenui's Processes of Decolonization the first step of Rediscovery and Recovery were mentioned in relation to the unfortunate yet not cemented nor irreversible phenomenon of "dealing with a traditional culture from the perspective of a foreign culture." In other words, when one or more people treat a traditional culture that is steeped in its principles and enriching factors as if it's foreign to what is relevant or "real" and therefore not only disowns the traditional practices of that culture but disavows that very culture as if it never existed.

In context to the human body and the practice of Trauma Cooperative Yoga®, or lack thereof, one is born with a certain amount of self-introspection and knowing of oneself. When a small child yells, "Mommy, my tummy hurts!" It's a call for support, but it's also a desire to call for attention to the source of the problem. However, when an adult oftentimes calls their doctor and says their stomach is ailing them it is oftentimes a call for a solution. Whereas, a child is often more capable of believing in there being a solution for all that ails both them, *and the world,* an adult oftentimes seeks to mask the problem with a bandaid solution due to being unwilling or without sufficient self-education to seek to discover what the *cause* of the problem might be in the first place. Adults are oftentimes conditioned to accept, or surrender to, the fate of a situation and work toward a solution instead of returning to the problem to see if the problem itself might contain the solution. One of the reasons for this difference is oftentimes the crossroads of *spirituality,* or the child's natural feeling of interconnectedness with everything, and *science,* or the adult's heavy reliance on facts procured by an outside source.

In his article about the stages of decolonization, Laenui writes, "Indigenous people themselves can abuse their own culture." This sentiment runs a parallel with the coinciding abuse that occurs within the context of one's relationship with one's own body. The foundation of absolute assurances for the solution to a problem that is contained within the human body is oftentimes disempowering for the patient, or wellness client. It can cause a disconnect between self and self-discovery. Laenui goes on to say, "especially when they have been so long and completely separated from the practice or appreciation from their traditional culture". The practice of self-reference in the determination of what is the root cause for illness or dis-ease has long gone by its wayside. Trauma Cooperative Yoga® asks the practitioner to clue into what's happening internally and relationally so as to weave in the what-is of a life situation, as well as what might be altered in order to support a return to health and wellness.

Although people are often seeking to be told what to do in the fitness arena, whether it be yoga or otherwise, it is in the best interest of both the health practitioner leading the program and the paying client to tune into the structure of their own physical, emotional, mental, and spiritual selves in order to find what works as a whole instead of just on one level of existence. In TCY® the process of delving inward and making choices based on the information that is being fed to them through their body is a nuanced one where all components of self are being inquired of. It is in this process of the recovery of the listening to self first and foremost that people's tendencies to distrust the self as a daily practice begins to dissolve. The question becomes where did this distrust from self begin as well as at what point did this relationship between cause and effect begin to fade?

The revolution to reunite people with their bodies, and be a director in the relationship building between one's awareness, and one's bodily self, is growing rampant around the world due to too many people giving away their instinctual power to the certainty of 'factual' knowledge as discerned by studies conducted, in the past, on past human bodies and lives. There are also too many news stories, movies, and printed literature about people who turned around their diagnosis of terminal illness, or the statement of never being able to walk again as given by the well-meaning doctor, only to continue not only living *but living more healthfully than ever,* Therefore, it is essential to consider the practice of TCY® and in the belief of rewriting our own narrative to self-connection. In the book, *The Pilates Body,* by the well sought out New York City trainer, Brooke Siler, she writes, "As strange as it may sound coming from a personal trainer, I do my best to promote self-sufficiency when it comes to exercise." She goes on to say, "We spend the majority of our lives trying to influence external forces over which we have little or no control, when the very thing over which we have complete control is literally beneath our own noses." (pg.12)

The everyday invisibility of the internal structure of the body often heightens the sense of unknown and therefore further creates a disconnect between experiencer and the experienced. The impetus to even try and form the bridge between the two is often disillusioned by the arrival of fear, uncertainty, and doubt, otherwise known as "FUD", as Randy Zales, former United States Army paratrooper turned performance consultant, iterates. The human potential factor for all people, in all countries, of all faiths, colors and creeds is enormously stupendous when one considers the "inner-listening" factor. For just as, "If we don't show up for ourselves then who will?" is an utterance of the author's so is the life-finding that if we refuse to *listen* to ourselves then what precedent are we setting for the people around us in the treatment *of ourselves?*

MOURNING, AS CALLED FOR BY LAENUI

In Poka Laenui's decolonization work, he writes about the essentialness of mourning in the journey of healing. Laenui also mentions the explosive moment of hearts combined to bring presence to the loss of the land known as Hawaii due to the deeply unsettling process known as colonization. The example he gives is of 10,000 people coming together at the Palace Iolani in January 1993 to mourn the loss of their land due to the colonizer's takeover. Laenui talks about the power of acknowledgment of what is lost and how it even accelerates the first phase of rediscovery and recovery. One might ask, "What was lost for you?" during this phase of our lives? And, "How have you dealt with this loss on a personal scale?"

People came from all over the world to be there at the palace while other natives sat by on their televisions and radios simultaneously holding space.

In *I AM THAT* by Sri Nisargadatta Maharaj, a discussion ensues of the vitality of whether it might be greater to love or to be loved. In this version a psychiatrist and general practitioner has traveled to India to speak with the Maharaj. The answer that is given by the Maharaj is, "I would rather have both! But I can see that to love is greater, nobler, deeper. To be loved is sweet, but it does not make one grow." (pg. 216) This is mentioned here because in this case perhaps mourning is an instrument of love. Mourning extends us to the farthest parameters of our grief, and in that it teaches us that love in its many forms can take us far. If we love, when we love, it delivers us to a place of greater power than we've known before. We feel more, we challenge ourselves more. We honor more of what we believe and we hold our convictions close. In this perspective, the mourning that Laenui speaks of makes an enormous amount of sense to be with in the face of not only speaking truth loud and clear for all to hear but also to feel the effects of other's actions enough that we know the counter force of intelligence and energy that is needed to persuade self and others in the opposite direction of violence.

This said, violence isn't always as visible as the chaining, raping, and murdering of villages. It is as soft a whisper as saying, *"You don't know"*, and *"You cannot change what-is"*. Wide sweeping violence is an eruption of human concern in the wrong direction, and benefits only a few, in the realm of a global nation as having the potential to be one. However violence might play out globally, nationally, locally, or within, on a personal scale we have the ability to stop violence from forming enough of a welt on our soul that we may still heartfully pursue the pleasures and decencies of life. Our abilities as people to go within and discover newly-fertile beginnings is endless. Our discovery of self, and inner peace or acceptance, *so that we might influence the world in the direction of our nobler desires,* is ever present.

In Trauma Cooperative Yoga® we accept the sting of the realities of life. We do not seek to be larger than the distraction, nor the cause of dis-ease. We work around it. We look at all that we are given informationally, from our inner-senses, and self-observances, and we figure out how we might move forward in a way that best honors both our need for self-recovery, and for mourning. In all truth, we can *never* live up to the forcefulness, or the expectations, of those who might know *'more'* or *'better'* than us. Voices outside of our own are founded on a different set of life experiences, and other people's knowledge-taking based on their own research. The more free choice is given up, the more negatively-distanced we become from our own inner-abilities to find our own way, and we need to learn to transcend projections of what leaders in power, in the yoga classroom or otherwise, tell us we 'should' do.

TCY® teaches us that at some point in our lives we will need to listen to ourselves in order to regain our equilibrium between being a pliable human being, and listening to our own friendly bottomline that seeks us to heed its call. The heart of TCY® and its vein of existence is self-love. For self-love to happen we need to regain our vital energy, for we need energy to pursue all change, both inwardly and outwardly. Sri Nisargadatta Maharaj writes, "Since time immemorial you loved yourself, but never wisely. Use your body and mind wisely in the service of the self; that is all. Be true to your own self: love yourself absolutely. Do not pretend that you love others as yourself. Unless you have realized them as one with yourself you cannot love them. Don't pretend to be what you are not; don't refuse to be what you are. Your love of others is the *result* of self-knowledge, not its cause. Without self-realization, no virtue is genuine." (pg. 187)

In *Trauma and Memory* by Peter Levine, he quotes William Faulkner's *Requiem for a Nun* in saying, "The past is never dead. It's not even the past." Levine goes on to say, "Rather, it lives as a panoply of manifold fears, phobias, physical symptoms, and illnesses." (pg. 7) If we are to mourn correctly and precisely, we need to follow in the footsteps of tribal cultures and use our bodies as a vehicle for shifting the tides of what is, and what is to be. As the body holds new truth that is earned through the living out of the embodiment of human expressiveness, possibilities shift. New narratives are built as we re-identify with our body selves as places of newfound safety and connection.

Since Yoga is the merging of mind and body, the physical posture of what is called "easy sitting pose", or any other seated posture for that matter, combined with the native practice of a sweat lodge, that are held in communities nationally, and internationally, can suffice to bring about both molecular and massive collective change. In order for real change to happen both the body and the mind need to be in concert through the emphasis of recurring communication processes. Yoga is a state of mind, and a practice that requires full self attention. In order for people to have less cause for suffering we must unite all sources of strength, and this agreeably includes mourning and rediscovery.

LAENUI'S DREAMING FOR DECOLONIZATION

For the vivid dreamer, dreams rarely have a clear beginning or end, for dreams are expansive enough that they exceed even one's own definition of what's real and what's possible. Dreams come to us by a force that can neither be reckoned with nor ever fully extinguished. For Laenui, in his decolonization process, he visions that, "the dreaming phase must be allowed to fully run its course. If the dreaming is cut short by any action plan or program designed to create a remedy meeting the perception of the issue at a premature stage, the result can prove disastrous." In yoga we see this, as well. If the yoga practitioner wants to attain the embodiment of a particular posture they've determined will help their practice grow to the *'next level'*, or will conjure great self-mastery, it is best to *slowly* inch one's way toward the vision of self. In yoga, there must be *more* than the goal to begin a posture, or to reach the 'end' or most advanced version of the posture. As facilitators of TCY®, we must further root into the practitioners' needs as the practitioner processes *the energies needed* in order to move toward the next posture, or embodiment of how one feels in the moment.

To be comfortable in one's body is essential for having the capacity to both dream, and effectively carry out the dream. However, oftentimes if we address the plans of our dreams with a lack of ease, inwardness, and connection then the attempts to flourish feel, seem, and look disjointed. A New York Times post article written by Allison Sadlier says that a recent study shows that more than fifty percent of people feel uncomfortable in their bodies. The top reason is body image with the last cause for discomfort listed as the content that people see in social media online. Part of colonizing a geographic area is to make the people think that there is something inherently wrong with them. This includes the way that the traditional culture's body looks, moves, and even dresses. Therefore, having stewardship over one's own body relationship is essential for the building of the dream at large.

In Hawaii, Laenui gives the example of a new convention being formed where the Hawaiian voice and self-determination of the Hawaiian people is being brought into sight. However, Laenui warns once again of rushing the outcome. He says, "Hawaii continues to face the threat of rushing the dream. Now that the topic of Hawaiian sovereignty has caught on as one of the foremost political issues of the day, many are demanding immediate action, with a belief that reflection and introspection are not worth the time and effort."

It is also such with the practice of yoga slowly becoming a more independently-minded although essentially community-founded practice. One cannot rush the idea that yoga is more than the physical postures, attaining the ultimate pose against all odds, or the beautification of the human body. Counter happenings, such as the rampant injuries that take place in studios that inadvertently push the practitioners to stretch to their maximum, or the simultaneous sexual and physical assault that happens, due to toxic power dynamics that dis-serve everywhere, *including in yoga studios,* are an admittedly sorrowful yet integral part of the unraveling of why a more *reflective* and *introspective* approach to yoga is necessary.

Whereas we have discovered yoga is for more than just men, contrary to what the roots of the practice originally deemed as being right or true, we must also stretch ourselves to see our own divinity and knowing, and set a precedent where this can be carried out on the mat in a supportive, and in tune, environment. It is with this inner-listening that we will learn that there are more considerations that need to be put into play than just following instructions to form the beginner, intermediate, or advanced version of the posture. Just as the words we speak matter, the basis of the formation of those words matter equally as such. Just as whether we begin or end a posture in a careful way matters, so does the meaningfulness of the posture, and the journey that carries that posture also matters, too. Just as the exact placement of the heel weighs in on the experience of the posture, so does the energy and emotion that makes it possible for that heel to be placed also matters, if not matters more.

The way of practicing TCY® is not just a collective or social issue, however those areas are affected by the practice of it on a regular and heartful basis, it is a *personal* one. If we were to rush to innerstand all the nuances of TCY® because we are zealous enough to want to try to do so in a matter of a few hours or months then we abate our learning. The learning curve becomes bent outward, and away from the practitioner. So, to Laenui's point, this emphasis on careful waiting, and integration, of one's dream is also a much needed approach in one's journey on the yoga mat.

COMMITMENT, AS INSPIRED BY LAENUI

In a *Psychology Today* article written by David Garner one's body image is referred to as being "our mental representation of ourselves." Garner goes on to say that, "Body image isn't simply influenced by feelings, and it actively influences much of our behavior, self-esteem, and psychopathology." Let's go as far to say that body image, if influenced by more than feelings, is also affected by our actions. In fact, when people report feeling well after practicing yoga it is likely because the body's actions are communicating to the practitioner in a mindful way that the practitioner of yoga is '*worth it*'. The practitioner is worth taking the time to focus on, love on, and improve upon. This can indeed change one's psychopathology, self-esteem, and in the long haul behavior. Perhaps, it is as simple as Sri Nisargadatta Maharaj says that in short once we truly love ourselves we can genuinely love another. Surely, if in more attention to oneself there is then more internal space to consider another then one might refrain from actively contributing to the creation of loss, or culture of maliceness to begin with.

Further on in the article, Garner reports, "The connection between sexual experiences and body image is affirmed in our overall findings. More than a third of all men (40 percent) and women (36 percent) say that unpleasant sexual experiences are moderately to very important in causing negative feelings in their body." The alteration of relationship between self and body in the event of negative bodily experiences, whether they be consensual or non consensual, as both reportedly affect people, is one of the causes for the TCY® mandate to be committed *to the use of agreeable language* that is incredibly careful not to shock, or re-member the original trauma, or negative experience, within the yoga practitioner on the yoga mat. The use of the word "massage" or "slide down" or "tap with fist", are all possibly triggering for the survivor of a negative physical experience. Hence, the decision of TCY® "to be ready for commitment to a single direction in which the society must move," as Poka Laenui says in the decolonization process. The action to come forward, and specify the very need for modification of approach, in such a tender way, is needed for change within the yoga community near and far.

The teaching of yoga itself is incredibly nuanced, and highly involved, and requires the voices of many leaders of yoga to weigh-in. One of the mainstays of the yoga community is a group called Yoga Alliance. They are a nationwide governing body confirming the certification, and degree of certification, of each teacher. They also formed to support the verification process of yoga schools. After YA has read the yoga school's curriculum the YA board decides whether they will stand behind the school's mandated curriculum, or not. They are an instrumental source of support for the yoga community and in sharing new voices, and are also a great platform for sounding off the call for a deeper look at what it is we decide we will individually and professionally take on from the original yoga teachings. TCY® is committed to widening the inclusivity for yoga practitioners, not only based on appearance, or skin color, or economic groups alone, but also for those with all different mental and emotional capacities. At the end of the day though, it is every yoga practitioner making the decision on their own or, *"exercising* self-determination," as Laenui says, that counts most. Surely, the "voices will weigh in" then.

LAENUI'S CALL FOR ACTION

Poka Laenui says in his five stages of decolonization, "While the first thought for independence would have been to grab the rifle and march against the colonizer, it seems the new weapons are dictated by technological development." Whereas partaking in rallies and protests against the sexism and rapist culture, that is yoga's lived past, such as the voice of abuse that was represented in the documentary *Bikram: Yogi, Guru, Predator - Inside his Empire of Abuse* is one option, another is to take dominion over one's own body again. This can be made possible in both seemingly small and large ways. If one constantly seeks opinion as to how to care for one's body, dress the body, color one's hair, and move about in one's own body to the degree that there is not an inch of room for movement outside of the outside suggestions made then one's *'seemingly small'* action is to determine movement. This might start on one's own personal yoga mat.

If one is supported in determining the final say on which way the energy of the body needs to move, then one is also given a torch to hold to light their path in making more ultimate decisions for the self *off of the mat,* too. Just as if one is encouraged to listen inwardly, instead of outwardly, it might present a sort of threat. From a governmental standpoint, there is a certain kind of danger in people moving about 'too' freely. For instance, if one finds one's liberation 'too readily' they might be less receptive to following in the suggested direction as is laid out by various officials on a variety of different levels.

For instance, and this is but one example, and is meant to lead in no place in particular, if the body does follow the mind, and the mind follows the body, then making the executive mental decision to move in a direction, as is best determined by the practitioner of yoga, and of life, must also affect the total self. Not only is the body able to follow a movement path that brings more energy to the self due to going about moving freely, but so are the mental and emotional selves able to feel more self-completion. This in and of itself is a technology that one is learning to develop from within. It is a technology founded on self-listening. The word technology itself stems from Greek culture, in the 1610s, meaning "a method of making or doing" as according to the *Online Etymology Dictionary*. In TCY®, our greatest resort to action is to create the means within ourselves from which we are able to then take action itself. This capability stems from having the energetic reserves within the self, *and self-acknowledgement,* first and foremost.

Although large group rallies and protests may or may not be the best course of action in the making of one's case for the cause of one's intention, and desire for change, it doesn't mean to take away all sense of showing up publicly for what we believe in and stand for. The word loitering in today's time has been represented in large red letters, and the presence of loitering signs, in and of themselves, are often enough to make any fair-minded person pick up the pace of their gait all on their own, no authority reminder needed in order to continue moving along. Unfortunately, the austerity of these signs can impact the freedom of movement of non-violent passersby. In these moments, the rigidity and severe self-discipline required of oneself, in order to ensure one doesn't pause for too long, that one might look suspicious to the untrained, or overly-mistrustful eye, only further aggravates one's daily disconnection to their bodily or personal needs.

When activity is directed from the outside, rather than from within, injury can happen and is often brimming on the horizon. A prime example is of when one never heeds the call to relieve their bladder when it is called for. The long term effects of this are actually life-deprecating and can cause weakened bladder muscles, urinary tract infections, and according to Susan A. Werner M.D. at Geisinger Nanticoke, "it can increase your risk of kidney disease and in rare cases even risk your bladder bursting—a condition that can be deadly." We might have formerly thought that not listening to our bodies is just a peripheral issue in one's life, and has no lasting effects. However, the list goes on. In this Geisinger-produced online article alone there are other effects mentioned from refraining to listen to the body's needs in the present moment.

Action can be difficult to take when we feel like we might be punished in some way or another, whether the possible punishment be through tactics of direct humiliation, or indirect forms of misrepresentation of another person, such as spoken or unspoken superiority-mindedness. This is why on the TCY® yoga mat we work to eradicate the language of "beginner, intermediate, advanced" as the reality is that oftentimes the most accelerated, or realized, thing someone can do is refrain from overworking themselves. Or, overworking their "go to" stance in strength-building, such as working the same muscle group, over and over each time that one comes into practice, and all because it's the so-called advanced version. In yoga, practitioners run the risk of leaping to their place of comfort which can be ironically enough in the most extroverted form of the posture that is being practiced. On the other hand, working from the base of a posture, or preliminary building steps, and pausing there is oftentimes more of a challenge for the yoga practitioner than it is to move fully into a posture at its "maxxed out version". The various embodiments of each posture require different strengths. It is hopefully known by now that strengths are both inwardly and outwardly cultivated. It is in the seeing of this nuance of yoga practice detail that we begin to best serve ourselves *and the people practicing with us.*

For a moment, let's return to the subject of loitering. Whereas publications such as Bloomberg's CityLab will give you information for how to "loiter legally", the question still becomes when did loitering become a perception of people stopping, pausing, talking, laughing, and joking? Although the impact of loitering laws influence everyone differently, and it is unlikely that people of significant means even notice the signs, it is still in question as to how necessary they even are when the posting of the signs have the potential of negatively affecting community development in areas that need it most. How much can someone's voice be heard, if where they may use their voice is so heavily controlled? Now, it is understood that as in the Bloomberg CityLab coverage "loitering" oftentimes refers to excessive noise, drinking, drugging, and selling illegal substances on the streets. However, if one is doing no such thing, nor intending to do any such thing of the nature, the restrictions themselves limit the place for people to convene, and connect, in order to therefore more develop their sense of connection that in turn leads to the sense of safety and overall well-being.

With so much red tape, *and red lettering,* affecting the convening of new and old friends alike on public land it predisposes people to have the necessity of money to partake in communal activities. If or when people do not have said monies to participate in community events, it very well likely can lead to pent up feelings of animosity and exclusion, and in the worst of cases hopelessness. These dispositions of self are markers for trouble. It is because of this that people now more than ever in our 'modern society' need to forage *for the very roots* of our existence, to feel our bodies, to connect to the presence of soothing wisdom within. This is possible when asked to self-listen. It is an almost inescapable freedom that people will come upon when asked to consider the inner source from which action springs.

In the name of action, it is essential to make TCY® inclusive. For the sake of a society at large, and how we all impact one another, we must consider one another. If money is an issue it is up to the TCY® leading practitioner to expand their circle of support so that the TCY® practice reaches everyone. Make TCY® accessible by conducting classes that are based on a monetary sliding scale. "What we sow, so shall we reap!" as is referred to in the Galatians 6 part of the Bible. In the Hindu culture, it's called karma. No matter how we wrap our heads around it, giving people the chance we had when becoming yoga practitioners and yoga teachers is a way to go full circle. We offer up our journeys, as people offer up theirs, and in turn enrich one another's lives full stop.

JOSEPHINE STANDING

IN THE NAME OF MOVEMENT: WE RISE, WE CALL, WE LISTEN TO LEARN...

Searching for the worldwide statistics on this issue and topic of the hindrance of limited range of movement might be too tedious of a task given there is such a wealth of information to tend to on the shores of the USA alone. So, we will start there and see where we branch out. Let it be known, this possible geographically-lessened investigation into the subject matter is of no reflection to lack of disinterest in nations prosperously existing and thriving beyond the United States borders. The possible constriction on research is just a reflection of needing to most solidly cover the subject matter in a way that benefits the focused comprehension for all present. This is after all a dense subject that requires deep learning.

Firstly, allow me to introduce the concept of ethnomathematics as envisioned by Newcomb Greenleaf. Greenleaf himself is an incredibly learned educator of our time in the twenty-first century. Not only does he have a PhD in Mathematics from Princeton University and a BA in Mathematics and Physics from Haverford College, he also became a renegade mathematician as he began to identify as a Temple Geometer in which he references Japanese Temple Geometry. He is well aware of the traumatization that math can incur, especially when blended with sexism or racism, and therefore spends his life making math more of a lived experience at Goddard College & University in Vermont.

The concept of ethnomathematics evolved from the need to address that classroom curriculums at present have little to nothing to do with what those practitioners later experience in life as people. According to Ubiratan D'Ambrosio in his work found through Research Gate, "Much of the content of current mathematics programs does little to help practitioners learn the information and skills necessary to function successfully in this new world." In the book, *Teaching Children Mathematics* by D'Ambrosio the following is clarified, The term ethno describes "all of the ingredients that make up the cultural identity of a group: language, codes, values, jargon, beliefs, food and dress, habits, and physical traits." Mathematics expresses a "broad view of mathematics which includes ciphering, arithmetic, classifying, ordering, inferring, and modeling." (pp. 2-3)

If ethnomathematics is a relationship between culture and mathematics then let us look at the impact of limited or repetitive movement on a particular culture, and why Trauma Cooperative Yoga® is such a useful tool for the afflicted. For the sake of a focused conversation here on this page let's look at the chosen country, for the moment, the United States of America. In order to really narrow down this investigative work, let us consider the United States military active duty and veterans. This group of people are surprisingly sensitive to having the lens on them, especially the veterans. However, the darkness of the unknown *must* be penetrated by the light of awareness. Otherwise, the unknown will fester in the dark, and without a doubt cause unspeakable injury.

Moving forward, one of the primary employers of military veterans are oil field companies. The challenge with that is that many veterans have injuries from their service years. So, compound that with the rigorous career choice of oil rigs and oil fields and it's a recipe for health disaster. In a simple search online with the key words, "oil fields hiring military veterans", although it's clearly going to direct one to ample information on the leading search words, civilians might be surprised at how heavily marketed these often health-damaging career choices are to our transitioning military members. For instance, there is a complete site online called Veterans Energy Pipeline. As of June 2021, their motto is, **A MESSAGE TO ALL VETERANS:THE OIL AND GAS INDUSTRY NEEDS YOUR ENERGY.**

Of course, there's nothing overtly wrong with the career choice of working in oil. However, in the time of mental and emotional fragility so many veterans are faced with experiencing post-service, at the time of transition, the enthusiastic, although surely well-meaning, encouragement to take on such work can feel akin to how many females often feel when going to buy a car at a sales-hungry lot. If it's not oil, then what other choices might we look at in this overarching view of work that promotes limited range of movement? For many, at the time of transition, in transition readiness programs and the like, as provided by the United States military, it is still working. Although a noble profession, and much needed in society, whether done by a computer's technological system or human beings living in the flesh, it is quite damaging long term.

An article, *Many oilfield injuries go unreported* by Lise Olsen with *The Houston Chronicle* reads, "Experts say national statistics about oilfield injuries generally *undercount* accidents." It goes on to say that one oil company known as, "Nabors Drilling USA has one of the highest number of worksite accidents reported to federal OSHA by U.S. employers involved in drilling, well service or petroleum extraction businesses," at least "according to reports in a U.S. Department of Labor enforcement database." In this said article, one story is told where the oilfield worker was challenged in receiving support for this lethal injury because the reported company said it never happened.

Often because of the lack of opportunity to constructively explore possible career possibilities, from a fully-present mental perspective, military veterans too often end up in positions with the most highly-reported workplace injury statistics. *Work Injury Source* cites these jobs as being the most statistically injury prone, Heavy truck and tractor-trailer truck drivers; Laborers and freight, stock, and material movers; Light truck drivers; Construction laborers; Maintenance and repair workers; Stockers and order fillers. Ironically, they all either require little body movement that is not repetitive, such as driving, stocking inventory, and mechanical repetitive movement like driving a hammer or screw into material.

So far, the culture is looking persuasive, in an unhealthy way, and deceptive, for those who answer the call to "give of their energy" to the jobs that are waved before transitioning military. This is again not to say there is anything in the least "wrong" with any of these jobs in and of themselves. However, one must enter the jobs with caring overseers who desire to fulfill their responsibility to those injured in the event of the occurrence of injury. In addition, these mentioned workplaces are meant to stymie the growth of potential threat by superseding grounds for injury with working conditions that promote healthfulness and wellbeing.

THE COMMON THREAD

All yoga practitioners, and followers of Laenui's work, must resolve to make the act of looking deeply a most commonplace disposition. *U.S. Bureau of Labor Statistics* data, as referenced by the *Work Injury Source* article, *Workplace Injury Statistics – 2020 Data for Workplace Accidents, Injuries, and Deaths* that was mentioned previously, states that **the most common of all causes for workplace injury is synchronistically the impetus for writing this body of work: overexertion and bodily reaction.** In the yogically-trained body, especially the Trauma Cooperative Yoga® practiced body, one is extensively guided to listen inwardly. This means that when one needs to replete one's energies, they are encouraged to do so, and in ways that best serve the innate sense of the cause for depletion in the first place.

Does this mean that said workers in said fields need to have more hydration nearby, sufficient rest periods on breaks, and possibly even yoga postures practiced on the suggested breaks? It is with firm belief that this is true. Especially, for the second cause mentioned which is bodily reaction. When a body and mind are tuned together as one working unit, then they effectively communicate. For better or for worse, when energy is flowing, and conducted with sufficient flow in the body, just as with a machine, the communication runs quicker, and deleterious reactions are replaced with conscious responses. If the noted workplace considerations are not being taken into consideration then it is safe to say the environment is being oppressive, and will remain to be rooted in oppression until the human needs of safety, replenishment, and body-health upkeep are being met.

In the event of military veterans feeling pressured to make ends meet, as soon as possible, upon completing work with the military, especially those service members retiring with families to feed, the chances of taking the fastest work offered are high. Perhaps, the leaders of said examples of highly labor-intensive jobs are even anticipating such need. Nevertheless, once the action is choiceful to begin such work, the conditions which one works from within are on the moral backs of all those who enjoy the fruits of the labors of said laborers. Another cause for military service members, transitioning out of their military branch of choice, to leap at the first chance at work, can be a byproduct of the *screamingly-large* numbers of those affected by Post Traumatic Stress.

More than twenty people who have served in the United States Military *per day,* every day of the year, are committing suicide. The question as to what the cause is for this rampant run for one's life arises for anyone who hears that statistic. Yet, the curiosity factor alone is not enough. Building highways, bridges, and dedicating buildings to those who have fallen is not enough. Guaranteeing support through the *Veteran's Affairs - VA* is not enough for many. Apparently, the solution has something to do with the transition process that service members undergo before leaving the military base of service itself. Whereas applying one's signature to exit paperwork, and watching *"death by powerpoint"* slides that contain information as to what next steps might look like for the transitioning service member is mandatory, that is about all that is.

If mind and body are one, as yoga believes, then the disciplined service member will do as asked, at the time of being requested to do as being told, however this also puts the body in a state of detachment from personal agency. If as Garner in, *Psychology Today,* says that body image really is more than mere feelings alone, but is a composition of behaviors (or actions) and psychopathology, then the identity of a transitioning service member is etched into the veteran's mind as being a follower of orders, compliant, and without personal reference to one's personal needs or considerations in the first place. Although this is ideal for recruiting service members into high risk positions, it leaves little room for personal enrichment.

Not only is the limited, or repetitive, range of movement an underlying health problem maker for many of the top "go to" jobs for countless American military service members, so is the forming of sound relationships. Although it can be difficult to find an exact percentage of how many military marriages result in divorce on the official-run website Military.com other sources give their knowledge. *MarketWatch* warns that Americans in the military service have the highest rate of divorce *before the age of thirty* of all the high stress fields of employment options. This is with a divorce rate of 30% or in other words nearly 1 in 3 people in the American military are likely to end their marriage in divorce!

The *MarketWatch* article goes on to say, "Mental health issues put additional strain on marriage, with 20% of Iraq and Afghanistan veterans reporting experiences with post-traumatic stress disorder and depression, experts say. Another study from Military.com — a website that gives people with a connection to the military access to jobs, benefits and discounts — found that even non-deployed military members found their relationships struggled due to marrying too young and moving too often." This said, for the military members who have fewer moves, and marry later in life, it is possible that by having more mind and body geared health solutions at the time of service, *and transition,* we might very likely see a decrease in the choices and actions that lead to injury later on. This observation goes for both the consideration of minor to serious injuries, as well as for the inclusion of a *decrease* in fatalities.

Although the limited range of movement that has been spoken about in this work is related to the freedom to move about in one's body as one is called to do or needs to do based on present moment felt information, the idea extends beyond that. Perhaps, if it weren't for the inability to come home to see family and friends during the course of service member deployments the personal connections, for the analyzed group reported in the study, might be maintained for longer periods of time, and exist in better standing. The inability to leave a high stakes military building when needing a break, or breath of fresh air, or to travel to the nearby state to see loved ones, indubitably impacts one's range of motion, and therefore felt sense to embody oneself completely.

These nuances of experience are oftentimes perceived as "just being a part of the moment" for military members in the dictated present moment. The rules serve to create cohesion, and reliable working standards, and certainly should not change. However, at the time of exit, or transition, it is essential for service members to be able to calculate the impact of the time spent at service duty stations. This can look like mandated participation in peer-supported body and mind centered exercises that ask the service member for their plans of full-self embodiment now that their service time is coming to an end. Whereas choice, and full-self consideration, was not always at the forefront of one's reality, what might the future hold?

Furthermore, what are the personally-recognized impressions of the service time years on their lives? What might one do as far as actions, behaviors, and habits go in order to further cement the desirable long lasting effects of the years served? On the flipside, what thought considerations might one apply to creating a plan *in written place* to solidify the counter thoughts, actions, and habits that might stymie one's best efforts to begin one's next life chapter? In the company of people who have faced similar experiences, the creation of strong plans is more likely to come to fruition. For one, we as people tend to step up our commitment to life when we sense we are in on the plan-making with others versus being alone.

In the event this modification to transition readiness programs is drawn into consideration by the respected officials, it will rectify the otherwise issue of service members being with one another for breakfast, lunch, and dinner, for years on end, only to see one another in a contactless class. These "death by powerpoint" situations are often with service members staring at the back of one another's heads, chin dropped down while looking at pre-printed worksheets, that require little-to-no written or spoken contribution, or eyes glued to projection screen. All of the mentioned enactments of current day military transition neither require nor call on participation in a healthful way. In these circumstances, both body and mind are shut down.

In the interest of society at large, and the ongoing abilities of both the service members themselves and the military itself, change must happen. This change must happen sooner than later. The confidence of the people in a nation that cares and comforts balances on the actions of the officials in control of such measures of change. In the words of Sri Nisargadatta Maharaj, "It is not theories and systems that I need; there are many equally attractive or plausible. I need a stirring of the heart, a renewal of life, not a new way of thinking." (pg. 215)

Bibliography:

Ackerman, Sandra. "Discovering the Brain." *National Center for Biotechnology Information*, U.S. National Library of Medicine, 1 Jan. 1992, www.ncbi.nlm.nih.gov/books/NBK234151/.

Adair, Bill. *The Emotionally Connected Classroom: Wellness and the Learning Experience*. Corwin, 2019.

Aisenstein, Marilia. "The Indissociable Unity of Psyche and Soma: A View from the Paris Psychosomatic School." *PubMed*, 2006, pubmed.ncbi.nlm.nih.gov/16854732.

API - American Petroleum Institute . (n.d.). *A MESSAGE TO ALL VETERANS:THE OIL AND GAS INDUSTRY NEEDS YOUR ENERGY*. Veterans Energy Pipeline. https://veteransenergypipeline.com/.

Arnsten, Amy, et al. "This Is Your Brain in Meltdown." *Scientific American*, U.S. National Library of Medicine, Apr. 2012, www.ncbi.nlm.nih.gov/pmc/articles/PMC4774859/.

A Secure Base, sites.uea.ac.uk/providingasecurebase/a-secure-base.

Attenborough, Sir D. A Life on Our Planet: My Witness Statement and a Vision for the Future. Grand Central Publishing, 2020.

Avery, Timothy. "Accountability." *Veterans Yoga Project*. 2019. Web. 13 Mar. 2021.

Basavaraddi, Ishwar V. "MEA: Search Result." *Ministry of External Affairs, Government of India*, Morarji Desai National Institute of Yoga, 23 Apr. 2015, www.mea.gov.in/search-result.htm?25096%2FYoga%3A_su_origen%2C_historia_y_desarrollo.

"Becoming Quotes by Michelle Obama." *Goodreads*. Goodreads. Web. 02 Oct. 2020.

Bullock, Grace. "What Focusing on the Breath Does to Your Brain." *Greater Good*, Greater Good Magazine, greatergood.berkeley.edu/article/item/what_focusing_on_the_breath_does_to_your_brain

Caplan, Heather, et al. "The Irony of Our Modern Female-Dominated Yoga." *Spright*, 2 Feb. 2016, archive.spright.com/exercises/history-of-women-practicing-yoga/.

Chambers, Andrew. "Mental Illness and Drug Addiction May Co-Occur Due to Disturbance in the Brain's Seat of Anxiety and Fear." *Https://www.apa.org*, American Psychological Association, 2 Dec. 2007, www.apa.org/news/press/releases/2007/12/amygdala.

Dagfinn, Moe. "Risk-takers Are Smarter, According to a New Study." *ScienceDaily*, 6 Oct. 2020, www.sciencedaily.com/releases/2015/11/151130113545.htm.

D'Ambrosio, U. (2001, February). *What is ethnomathematics, and how can it help children in schools?* Research Gate. https://www.researchgate.net/publication/284702127_What_is_ethnomathematics_and_how_can_it_help_children_in_schools.

Elisha, Perrin. The Conscious Body: A Psychoanalytic Exploration of the Body in Therapy. United States, American Psychological Association, 2011.

Emotional Contagion: What It Is and How to Avoid It. (n.d.). Retrieved October 2, 2020, https://www.healthline.com/health/emotional-contagion

EOC Institute – Access Deep Meditation Quickly, Safely, & Easily, EOC Institute, eocinstitute.org/meditation/meditation-can-make-you-more-social/.

Gach, Michael Reed, and Beth Ann Henning. *Acupressure for Emotional Healing: a Self-Care Guide for Trauma, Stress & Common Emotional Imbalances*. Bantam Spectra, 2005.

Garner, D. (1997, February 1). *Body Image in America: Survey Results.* Psychology Today. https://www.psychologytoday.com/us/articles/199702/body-image-in-america-survey-results.

Gibson, Andrea. "Andrea Gibson Quote." *Lib Quotes*, libquotes.com/andrea-gibson/quote/lbv4u4a.

Goldman, Bruce. "Researchers Pinpoint Brain Circuitry Underlying Dissociative Experiences." *News Center*, Stanford Medicine , 16 Sept. 2020, med.stanford.edu/news/all-news/2020/09/researchers-pinpoint-brain-circuitry-underlying-dissociation.html.

Griswold, Eliza. "Yoga Reconsiders the Role of the Guru in the Age of #MeToo." *The New Yorker*, www.newyorker.com/news/news-desk/yoga-reconsiders-the-role-of-the-guru-in-the-age-of-meto o.

Grigoriadis, Vanessa. "Yogi John Friend's Karmic Crash -- New York Magazine - Nymag." *New York Magazine*, New York Magazine, 13 Apr. 2012, nymag.com/news/features/john-friend-yoga-2012-4/.

Hadjistavropoulos, Thomas, and Kenneth Craig. *Pain: Psychological Perspectives*. 1st ed., Psychology Press, 2003.

Hamilton, Diane Musho. "Calming Your Brain During Conflict." *Harvard Business Review*, 16 Feb. 2016, hbr.org/2015/12/calming-your-brain-during-conflict.

Hammond, Holly. "The Timeline and History of Yoga in America." *Yoga Journal*, 29 Aug. 2007, www.yogajournal.com/yoga-101/yogas-trip-america.

Health Psychology Service, Chesterfield PCT. (2013) *The Gate Control Theory of Pain Ver3.0*. Center for Integrative Healthcare. VA Healthcare Information. https://www.mirecc.va.gov/cihvisn2/Documents/Patient_Education_Handouts/Gate_Control_Theory_of_Pain_Version_3.pdf

Herman, Judith. *Trauma and Recovery: The Aftermath of Violence-From Domestic Abuse to Political Terror*. New York: Basic, 1992. Print.

Herman, Judith Lewis. *Trauma and Recovery: The Aftermath of Violence--From Domestic Abuse to Political Terror*. 1R ed., Basic Books, 2015.

Hesse, Hermann. *Siddhartha*. Simon & Brown, 2012.

Horan, Roy. "The Neuropsychological Connection Between Creativity and Meditation." *ResearchGate*, May 2009, www.researchgate.net/publication/253976833_The_Neuropsychological_Connection_Between_Creativity_and_Meditation

"How Improvisation Changes the Brain." *Psychology Today*, 1 Oct. 2019, www.psychologytoday.com/us/blog/play-your-way-sane/201910/how-improvisation-changes-the-brain.

“How the Brain Enables Us to Rapidly Focus Attention.” *ScienceDaily*, ScienceDaily, 27 Dec. 2018, www.sciencedaily.com/releases/2018/12/181227102057.htm.

“Humanistic Psychology.” *Wikipedia*, Wikimedia Foundation, 2 Sept. 2020, en.wikipedia.org/wiki/Humanistic_psychology.

"Impacts of Psychological Security, Emotional Intelligence and Self-Efficacy on Undergraduates’ Life Satisfaction | Afolabi | Psychological Thought." *Psychological Thought*, psyct.psychopen.eu/index.php/psyct/article/view/226/html?acceptCookies=1

Iyengar, B.K.S. *Light on Life: The Yoga Journey to Wholeness, Inner Peace, and Ultimate Freedom*. Rodale, 2006.

Jabr, Ferris. "Why Your Brain Needs More Downtime." *Scientific American*, 15 Oct. 2013, www.scientificamerican.com/article/mental-downtime/#.

Joseph, Stephen. "Why Being Yourself Matters." *Psychology Today*, Sussex Publishers, 28 Oct. 2017, www.psychologytoday.com/us/blog/what-doesnt-kill-us/201710/why-being-yourself-matters.

"JRI/COVID-19 Navigator." *JRI Leader in Social Justice*. Web. 13 Mar. 2021.

Jung, C. G. *Liber Novus*. W. W. Norton & Company, 2012.

Kasanoff, Bruce. "Emotions Are Contagious, So Start Acting Much More Positively." *Forbes*. Forbes Magazine, 12 Nov. 2019. Web. 02 Oct. 2020.

Klein, Colin. *What the Body Commands: The Imperative Theory of Pain (The MIT Press)*. 1st ed., The MIT Press, 2015.

Kolk, Van Bessel. *The Body Keeps the Score: Brain, Mind, and Body in the Healing of Trauma*. Illustrated, Penguin Books, 2015.

Laenui, P. (2006, May 3). Processes of Decolonization . https://www.sjsu.edu/people/marcos.pizarro/courses/maestros/s0/Laenui.pdf.

Lambert, Jonathan. "Scientists Find Brain Cells That Make Pain Hurt." *NPR*. NPR, 17 Jan. 2019. Web. 13 Mar. 2021.

"Legend Sayings and Quotes." *Legend Sayings and Legend Quotes | Wise Old Sayings*, www.wiseoldsayings.com/legend-quotes/

Lenzen, Manuela. "Feeling Our Emotions." *Scientific American*. 01 Apr. 2005. Web. 12 Mar. 2021.

Levine, Jessica. "The Science of Breathing." *Yoga Journal*, 17 June 2015, www.yogajournal.com/yoga-101/science-breathing.

Levine, Peter. *Healing Trauma: A Pioneering Program for Restoring the Wisdom of Your Body*. Lexington, KY. ReadHowYouWant, 2012. Print.

Levine, Peter. *Trauma and Memory: Brain and Body in a Search for the Living Past: A Practical Guide for Understanding and Working with Traumatic Memory*. Illustrated, North Atlantic Books, 2015.

Levine, Peter. *Waking the Tiger: Healing Trauma: The Innate Capacity to Transform Overwhelming Experiences*. Berkeley, CA: 1997, North Atlantic Books.

Lowen, Alexander. *The Voice of the Body*. The Alexander Lowen Foundation, 2012.

Maharaj, N., Frydman, M., & Dikshit, S. S. (2012). *I am that.* Acorn Press.

Marshall, A. (2014, September 23). Bloomberg.com. https://www.bloomberg.com/news/articles/2014-09-23/a-guide-to-legal-loitering.

Melzack, R. "Pain and the Neuromatrix in the Brain." *Journal of Dental Education*. U.S. National Library of Medicine, Dec. 2001. Web. 12 Mar. 2021.

MIT - Massachusetts Institute of Technology. (n.d.). Bible Gateway Galatians 6 :: NIV. http://web.mit.edu/jywang/www/cef/Bible/NIV/NIV_Bible/GAL+6.html.

Moore, James W. "What Is the Sense of Agency and Why Does It Matter?" *Frontiers in Psychology*, Frontiers Media S.A., 29 Aug. 2016, www.ncbi.nlm.nih.gov/pmc/articles/PMC5002400/.

Moyer, Nancy. "Amygdala Hijack: What It Is, Why It Happens & How to Make It Stop." *Healthline*, www.healthline.com/health/stress/amygdala-hijack.

Naylor, Jennifer C., et al. "Self-Reported Pain in Male and Female Iraq/Afghanistan-Era Veterans: Associations with Psychiatric Symptoms and Functioning." *Pain Medicine*, 2017, p. pnw308. *Crossref*, doi:10.1093/pm/pnw308.

Oden, Michael S. When Nobody's Home, Understanding Human Behavior: The Workbook, Torrance, CA: 2018, Communication Shift Books.

Olsen, L. (2015, January 6). *Many oilfield injuries go unreported.* Houston Chronicle. https://www.houstonchronicle.com/news/houston-texas/houston/article/Many-oilfield-injuries-go-unreported-5980350.php#photo-7318426.

"On Math and Meditation." *QC Voices*, 9 Apr. 2015, qcvoices.qwriting.qc.cuny.edu/tamarlichter/2015/04/08/on-math-and-meditation/

Paul, K. (2018, February 26). *Americans in this field have the highest rate of divorce by age 30.* MarketWatch. https://www.marketwatch.com/story/employees-in-this-field-have-the-highest-rate-of-divorce-2017-07-13.

Pert, Candace. "How Meditation Lowers Social Anxiety, Raises Confidence."

"Pneuma | Origin and Meaning of Pneuma by Online Etymology Dictionary." *Online Etymology Dictionary | Origin, History and Meaning of English Words*, www.etymonline.com/word/pneuma.

Potter, Paul. Psyche and Soma: Physicians and Metaphysicians on the Mind-body Problem from Antiquity to Enlightenment. United Kingdom, Clarendon Press, 2002.

"Psyche and Soma: New Insights into the Connection." *PubMed Central* (PMC), 1 Jan. 2010, www.ncbi.nlm.nih.gov/pmc/articles/PMC3146208.

Ray, Amit. *OM Chanting and Meditation*. INNER LIGHT PUBLISHERS, 2010.

"Relational Integrative Psychotherapy." *Wiley Online Library*, www.onlinelibrary.wiley.com/doi/book/10.1002/9781119141518.

"Respiratory Failure." *NHLBI, NIH*, www.nhlbi.nih.gov/health-topics/respiratory-failure.

Roig-Franzia, Manuel. "Scandal Contorts Future of John Friend, Anusara Yoga." *The Washington Post*, WP Company, 28 Mar. 2012, www.washingtonpost.com/lifestyle/style/scandal-contorts-future-of-john-friend-anusara-yo ga/2012/03/28/gIQAeLVThS_story.html.

Rothschild, Babette. *8 Keys to Safe Trauma Recovery: Take-Charge Strategies to Empower Your Healing (8 Keys to Mental Health)*. 1st ed., W. W. Norton & Company, 2010.

Sadlier, A. (2020, February 18). *Most Americans admit they're not comfortable in their own skin*. New York Post. https://nypost.com/2020/02/18/most-americans-admit-theyre-not-comfortable-in-their-own-skin/.

Sanderson, A. (2003, October 27). The Case for Spirit Release. Retrieved March 12, 2021, from https://www.rcpsych.ac.uk/search?indexCatalogue=search&searchQuery=Dr.+Alan+Sanderson&wordsMode=AllWords

"Seane Corn Quotes (Author of Revolution of the Soul)." *Goodreads*, Goodreads, www.goodreads.com/author/quotes/2749054.Seane_Corn.

Sharma, Hari. "Meditation: Process and Effects." *PubMed Central (PMC)*, Wolters Kluwer -- Medknow Publications, 2015, www.ncbi.nlm.nih.gov/pmc/articles/PMC4895748/ "The Deeper Meaning of Aloha." *September/October 2020* | H U N A F R O M H A W A I I, 9 Nov. 2001, www.huna.org/html/deeper.html.

Sharon Martin, LCSW. "The Need to Please: The Psychology of People-Pleasing." *Psych Central*, Psych Central, 24 Jan. 2020, psychcentral.com/blog/imperfect/2020/01/the-need-to-please-the-psychology-of-people-pleasing.

Siler, B. (2000). *The Pilates body: the ultimate at home guide to strengthening, lengthening, and toning your body --without machines*. Broadway Books.

Standing, Jo. *Conquer Trauma Drama: Breakthrough Curriculum.* CreateSpace Independent Publishing Platform, 2017.

Standing, Jo. *Conquer Trauma Drama: Get Your Life Back.* 1st ed., Adventures In Ink, International, 2015.

Steffen-Russo, Anne. Answers for Sensitive People: Stories & Exercises to Live Life with More Harmony and Balance. United States, Self-Published, 2012

Summer Allen. "The Sharing Effect." *Greater Good*, 24 Nov. 2024, greatergood.berkeley.edu/article/item/the_sharing_effect.
technology (n.). Online Etymology Dictionary. (n.d.). https://www.etymonline.com/word/technology.

The Mindfulness Solution to Pain: Step-by-Step Techniques for Chronic Pain Management by Jackie Gardner-Nix (7-May-2010) Paperback. New Harbinger (7 May 2010), 2021.

Tugsbaatar , U. (2021, March 22). *Albert BANDURA: Self-efficacy for AGENTIC positive psychology*. PositivePsychology.com. https://positivepsychology.com/bandura-self-efficacy/.

Werner, M.D., S. A. (2018, March 29). Stop holding it in! 4 bodily functions you should let out. https://www.geisinger.org/health-and-wellness/wellness-articles/2018/03/29/21/13/stop-holding-it-in-4-bodily-functions-you-should-let-out.

Wis. (2021, March 14). *Workplace Injury Statistics - 2020*. Work Injury Source. https://workinjurysource.com/workplace-injury-statistics-2019/.

Wiseman, Liz. "Multipliers: How the Best Leaders Make Everyone Smarter." *Multipliers: How the Best Leaders Make Everyone Smarter*. New York, NY: HarperBusiness, an Imprint of HarperCollinsPublishers, 2017. 87-122. Print.

"Word Association: Princeton Study Matches Brain Scans with Complex Thought." *Princeton University*, The Trustees of Princeton

University, www.princeton.edu/news/2011/08/31/word-association-princeton-study-matches-brain-scans-complex-thought.

"Why Mouse Matters." *Genome.gov*. National Institutes of Health NIH, 23 July 2010. Web. 14 Mar. 2021.

About The Author

Jo happily lives with her U.S. Navy engineer husband, and wide-roaming Great Pyrenees pups, and has proudly served the Yoga world in both the USA and Canada since 2005. In 2003, she attended her first yoga studio class. As a recent trauma survivor on many levels, in the company of a classroom of unaffected civilians, she was crushed rather than uplifted by the traditional practice of yoga. She works to change that so that there are more adaptations, in light of the survivor, to the otherwise perfect health modality that Yoga is for all of humankind.

Made in the USA
Columbia, SC
08 November 2021

48585618R00155